Hurry Henrietta

Hurry
Henrietta

by MOLLY CONE

HOUGHTON MIFFLIN COMPANY BOSTON

CONTENTS

In a house on Lombard
Street in Baltimore,
1878, lived a family
with five girls.
Henrietta was seventeen
years old; Rachel,
thirteen; Sadie, ten;
Bertha, five; and Adele,
two . . .

Hurry Henrietta

1
The Medal

"*Dinner!*"

Maggie's voice, shouting up the narrow winding stairway to the bedrooms on the third floor, was followed by the faint sound of Mama ringing the dinner bell.

Guiltily Henrietta slammed her bureau drawer shut.

As she hurried down the two flights of stairs to the dining room on the first floor, she heard Bertha's plaintive tone, "Where's Henrietta?"

"She's late," Rachel said.

"Henrietta's never late," Sadie was saying as Henrietta flew through the dining-room door.

She took her seat. The Sabbath candles were already burning. Mama lit the twin candles on Friday

evening at the first hint of darkness, saying the prayer
of the lights standing with her hands in front of her
eyes.

Papa said the blessing over the cup of wine, and
added a little speech to Mama. It was from the Book
of Proverbs and Papa held up his glass of wine as if
it were a toast. He called Mama "a woman of valor."
"Her worth is far above rubies," he said, looking at
her admiringly.

Papa was thin with a dark complexion and not at
all tall, but when Papa talked people always listened.
His voice filled their dining room as he blessed the
bread and passed it around.

Mama's round cheeks glowed pink and her blue
eyes shone bluer. She is pretty, Henrietta thought
suddenly. Henrietta took after her father, everyone
said. She had always been a sallow little thing with
steadfast brown eyes and plain brown hair. Rachel
was the pretty one. Henrietta glanced down to the
foot of the table where Rachel sat dreamily staring up
at the faded wallpaper.

In their house, Mama sat at the head of the table,
and Papa at her right. Mama carved and dished
things out.

Henrietta's place was next to Papa, and Adele's
high chair next to her.

"My friend at school goes to see her cousins every Saturday," Bertha said loudly from across the table.

Bertha sat next to Sadie. The two little girls shared that side of the big table together.

"That's nice." Mama put some noodles on her plate.

"Why can't I go to see my cousins on Sunday?"

"Because they live in Europe, silly," Rachel answered for Mama.

"You mean that's too far to walk?"

Rachel laughed. "It's a swim. There's a whole ocean between here and Europe."

Bertha's eyes were wide and unbelieving. "Well, how did we get here?"

"You were born here."

"Henrietta, too?"

"All five of you," Mama said.

"But Papa and Mama came on a boat," Sadie said.

Mama handed her a plate. "Papa was seasick."

"It was a very rough voyage in those days." Papa helped himself to another piece of the twisted bread freshly baked for the Friday night dinner. It was the bread he had blessed and served to everyone at the start of the dinner. He broke off a big piece, sniffed with pleasure at its fragrance, and ate it daintily as if it were cake.

"Papa was very sick. It kept me from finishing *The Vicar of Wakefield.*" Mama pronounced the title of her book importantly. "I took it with me to read on the ship."

"So you had to finish it after you got here," Bertha prompted.

Papa only smiled and went on eating in the thoughtful way he did everything.

"I didn't have time after I got here!" Mama looked around severely as if it were everyone's fault.

"It was a good story." Henrietta had read it all through one day sitting in the deep, black leather chair in Papa's study.

"I thought it was dull!" Rachel made a face. "I didn't finish it either."

Mama frowned. "If you start something, you should finish it."

"Like Henrietta," Bertha put in.

Rachel looked at her mother and opened her mouth —

Mama said hastily, "If you're a mother, it's different. When you have a husband and children and a house, you have no time to read. But a young girl — " Mama left the sentence unfinished to make a clicking sound with her tongue.

"Henrietta always finishes everything she begins —" Sadie was matter-of-fact.

Rachel rose from her chair. "Henrietta-Henrietta-Henrietta! That's all I ever hear around here!"

Henrietta blinked. Papa looked surprised, but Mama regarded Rachel calmly. "Henrietta is the oldest," she said as if that explained everything.

Bertha nodded. "That's why Henrietta does everything best."

"But I don't sing best," Henrietta said hastily. "Rachel sings best."

"Sit down, Rachel," Mama said. "And pass me your plate."

Rachel sat down.

"And why should Henrietta have to sing?" Mama put some more lemon-stewed fish on Rachel's plate and passed it back. "She plays the piano and that's enough."

"But I like to sing." Henrietta felt annoyed all over again that she couldn't hold a tune.

"So some day you'll take a little time and practice," Mama said comfortably.

It didn't seem to make much difference how much she practiced, Henrietta thought. When she sang loudly, everybody made faces at her — even Mr. Deems, the singing teacher at the high school. Once he had even asked her to stop.

Maggie came in and took away an empty platter. Lizzie was right behind her carrying a bowl of

Mama's pickled tomatoes. Maggie and Lizzie lived in the house. They helped.

Mama had brought all her mother's recipes with her when she came as a bride to America. Their Baltimore cellar was full of her jellies and preserves, her pickled tomatoes and cucumbers and sauerkraut. Mama was a *hausfrau*. There was no one in the small German community of Baltimore who had not heard of her coffee kuchen and sponge cake.

"I heard that Mrs. Rosenfeld's daughter is going with a young man from the new university," Mama said.

Papa frowned. He never liked gossip at their dinner table.

Mama didn't count such news gossip. "He's a very nice boy!"

"And who says that he isn't?"

Mama smiled carefully. "It's nice that the university opened right here in our neighborhood."

"A fine thing for the city." Papa said.

They weren't talking about the same thing, Henrietta knew. Papa was a Rabbi and a scholar. He was always writing or lecturing when he wasn't busy leading his congregation, and he could read in several languages. She could see why he was pleased that the Johns Hopkins had recently opened its doors.

"I think it's a fine thing too," Rachel said eagerly. Henrietta looked at her.

"You mean because of the boys," Sadie said.

Uncomfortably, Henrietta stared down at her plate. She had already met one of them that afternoon, but she didn't mention it. She had met him on Eutaw Street. He wore a striped jacket and carried a book bag and was walking with Elizabeth Burkley. Elizabeth had introduced them.

"I'm going to the university here," he had said importantly.

Henrietta had felt a lurch of envy. "I wish I could go!"

"It's a school for *men*." He was amused at her. Education for women wasn't considered very important in Baltimore in 1878.

"That doesn't stop me from wishing women could go!"

"Henrietta's smart! She won the graduation medal at our high school," Elizabeth told him.

"Is that so?" He stared.

"Show it to him, Henrietta."

Henrietta hesitated. Then she pulled at the ribbon around her neck. She felt her face turning red when she held the gold disk up so he could see her name on it.

It was the very highest award, but she didn't say
so. It was given for excellence in languages, litera-
ture and mathematics.

He gave a whistle of appreciation. "Say! That's
something!"

"And she writes too!"

Uneasily Henrietta glanced at Elizabeth.

"You mean poetry?"

Henrietta shook her head. "Not exactly. It was an
article. I didn't really expect they would publish it."

"Frank writes beautiful poetry." Elizabeth's
voice was soft with admiration.

He smiled. "Oh, but I can't boast of anything pub-
lished."

"I wasn't boasting," Henrietta said quickly, then
bit her lip, for of course he hadn't meant it that way.

"You don't have to." Elizabeth sounded positive.
"Anyone can tell you're serious. Can't they, Frank?"
She pretended to sigh deeply. "Now me, anybody
can tell I'm not a *bit* serious."

Frank gazed down at Elizabeth and laughed. It
was an admiring laugh. Henrietta heard its echo
over the dinner table.

"Henrietta, you forgot your medal!" Sadie's voice
made everyone turn.

Henrietta looked down although she knew it was

not there. She had taken it off and pushed it into the
back corner of her bureau drawer.

"I didn't forget it. I just decided not to wear it
anymore."

"But you always wear it!"

Henrietta felt everyone looking at her.

"Did you lose it?" Mama was surprised.

Henrietta shook her head. She couldn't tell them
she had hidden it from her sight. She remembered
how proud Papa had been sitting among the dig-
nitaries on the platform of Ford's Grand Opera House
at her graduation exercises. She had earned the highest grade of any girl ever graduated from the Western
Female High School. Mr. Hollingshead, the princi-
pal, had presented the Peabody Medal to Henrietta with a bow and Papa had beamed the whole
time Henrietta made her speech. For some reason,
she couldn't look at Papa now.

"If I had a beautiful gold medal I'd wear it all the
time," Bertha said.

"Well, I wouldn't," Sadie said. "I'd lay it on a
bed of cotton and put it in a box, and tie a big ribbon
around it and keep it forever."

Rachel snorted.

Suddenly, Henrietta wanted to cry.

If she had been Rachel, she might have jumped

up and run out. Or, Bertha, she would have opened her mouth wide and wept loudly right at the table.

But she only stared unblinkingly at her plate, and finally went on eating her dinner.

Because she was Henrietta.

2
A Boy in a Striped Jacket

"Mama says come pass the cake!" Rachel's loud whisper reached to the top of the stairs.

Henrietta came down slowly. She grimaced at the parlor door.

It was Saturday. Saturday was the Sabbath in the Szold household. On the Sabbath, ladies from the congregation filled the parlor gossiping and nibbling at Mama's sponge cake.

The parlor with its stiff chairs, wax flowers and family album was a room Henrietta had never liked. It was used only for company. Henrietta still grew red when she had to talk to company. Reluctantly, she followed Rachel in.

Taking the plate of cake Mama gave her, she slowly moved around the room. Papa was leaning against the mantel talking. He was telling everybody about Henrietta's first article. Henrietta pretended not to hear.

She had written it as a letter and sent it to a periodical in New York, which often printed pieces of opinion like it. It had appeared in print as an article and the editor had written her asking for more.

"So you're the writer!" One of the ladies peered at her closely.

Henrietta felt her face growing as red as a Mexican rose in Papa's garden. Was she a writer? She didn't really know. She wished she could be. Papa would be pleased.

She had been writing summaries of her father's sermons for the newspapers ever since she had entered high school. She often helped Papa by copying out his sermons for him. He had taught Henrietta how to read the Hebrew books in his study and the German ones too. Papa had taught her how to "think."

She continued around the room holding a polite smile on her face for the visitors, but she was no longer seeing them. She saw herself, sitting on the sofa, with a young man in a striped jacket beside her. She saw herself talking with him. Probably he would be surprised at her clear thinking and wide knowledge — considering she was a girl, that is. She could just see his face, looking down at her, washed with amazement —

Her elbow moved sharply and the cake joggled on the plate.

"You're grinning!" Rachel whispered with another nudge. "You're standing there grinning at nothing at all!"

Hastily Henrietta looked around. Murmurs were rising and heads were turning — but not toward her. Bertha was standing in the doorway, her hair in curls, her best slippers on her feet and the giggles already making her starched petticoats shake. Bertha liked to come in to see the ladies.

But Sadie didn't. She quietly stole in behind Bertha. Her great dark eyes searched the room quickly to find Henrietta, and having found her, she seemed content to just stand and observe.

In a few moments, Henrietta knew, Lizzie would follow with Adele. Sometimes Adele cried when she was being shown to the visitors. She didn't like to be poked at by strange people either.

"Five girls!" one of the ladies said looking at them all. She stood, *tching* with her tongue at the sight of so many daughters. As if it were a sight to be sorry for, thought Henrietta.

"At least one of them should have been a son!" another lady said.

Mama only smiled and passed some more cake.
But Papa put his hand on Henrietta's shoulder and
said proudly, "Henrietta is my 'son.' "

Rachel had escaped to the kitchen and as soon as
she could, Henrietta followed.

"I wish I were Papa's son. Then I'd be going to
Johns Hopkins too!"

"Well, Papa sent you to high school." Rachel
pinched at a piece of cake and licked her fingers.
"Most people don't even consider high school very
important for girls."

Papa had. But the Western Female High School
was right there in Baltimore, Henrietta reflected,
while the nearest college for women was Vassar, in
New York.

"They've gone!" Sadie came in to report.

"Maybe we should say a blessing," Rachel said
recklessly.

Henrietta didn't even frown. She was thinking
of Vassar. Behind her the girls went out and upstairs, but Henrietta stood staring at the plates on
the kitchen table, waiting to be washed until the Sabbath was over.

Mama looked in. Mama hardly ever stepped into
the kitchen on the Sabbath.

Impulsively, Henrietta faced her. "Mama, can I
go to Vassar?" But she knew the answer before

Mama had time to open her mouth.

Mama was the manager. She was the one who kept careful account of what came in and what went out of the family purse. Mama always did all the shopping, going to the Lexington Market herself, with Henrietta along sometimes to carry the basket. Mama had taught Henrietta to keep strict notation of every penny she spent, even for stamps or hair ribbons. It was her mother's good management that had provided the funds for the publication of her father's special sermons and for the scholarly books in his study.

"Your Papa is not a rich man. He is a Rabbi with a Rabbi's salary," Mama told her.

But Henrietta didn't really need to be reminded.

The door bell rang again then, and automatically Mama looked to see how much cake was left.

Reluctantly, Henrietta moved down the narrow passage to the front door, trying to adjust her face to a company smile.

But the Sabbath caller was not another dressed-up lady from her father's congregation. It was a young man in a striped jacket. She gaped at him.

He stood there grinning at her as if she should know him. "Philadelphia," he said helpfully.

For a moment, Henrietta couldn't even think of who they knew in Philadelphia.

"Try Jastrow!" His eyes gleamed impishly.

Dr. Jastrow was Rabbi Szold's old friend. Henrietta had a picture suddenly of his two small sons, Joe and Morris. They had come with their father on a visit. She remembered Joe had had a stomachache and Mama had given him tea.

"Joe Jastrow?"

"And you're Henrietta!"

"How is your stomach?" She grinned a little too.

He laid his hand over his middle with a little grimace. "To tell you the truth — did I really have a stomachache?"

"As I remember, it was a headache too."

He put his hand to his head. "I think I've grown out of the stomachaches but —"

"Come in! Come in!" Papa called heartily. Rachel came running down too.

"I'm here to go to the new university," Joe told them all.

"I know," Henrietta smiled wryly, and suddenly it felt stiff on her face.

"I'll tell Mama to put on another plate for supper," Papa said.

"Thank you, but I can't stay that long. Not tonight, that is."

"Another time then," Papa said.

"Thank you!" His eagerness made Papa laugh.

Papa went back into his study. There were double doors between it and the parlor. Papa closed them.

"I read your article," Joe said to Henrietta.

She hadn't signed it with her name. She had used *Sulamith*. The pen name came from the Song of Songs in Papa's Bible.

"Return, return, O Shulamite . . ." she had often read the verse aloud in tones of high drama. Usually Rachel yawned before it was over, but Sadie and Bertha always clapped.

"How did you know it was mine?"

"Your father sent us a copy."

She knew Papa had been proud of her, but she hadn't expected him to go around talking so much about it. She felt pleased.

"Everyone says it's a good article," Joe said.

As if she were following the lines in a play, Henrietta sat down on the sofa and smiled modestly.

"Interesting subject." He came to sit down beside her.

Henrietta took a deep breath and tried not to smile too widely.

Her article had been on materialism. She had often talked about it with Papa. How so many people seemed to be busy acquiring things intead of ideals, as if happiness could be bought like lettuce at the market. She had thought about it a great deal

and written with honest fervor. The editor had called
it "timely."

"But I don't agree with you at all," Joe said.

She stared at him.

"You wrote as if materialism were the root of all
evil, so to speak. As if it were a cause. It's not, you
know," he said confidently. "It's merely a symptom
— like the red spots of a rash." His words bounced
out, with short bursts of laughter, and a droll expression.

Henrietta shook herself a little. When she spoke,
she spoke firmly. She told him exactly why she had
said what she had said. She had very good reasons.
Even Papa had thought so.

But Joe went right on arguing. He compared his
theory to the time he had the measles. He liked to
talk about himself, Henrietta noticed. He made a
game out of the discussion, laughing often. He was
enjoying himself. Even Mama could see that when
she came in to join them.

But Joe wouldn't change his mind about staying,
even with Mama's invitation. He laughed and teased
with Mama, too, just as if she were a girl, and he
winked at Rachel.

"My, he's a nice boy," Mama said when he had
gone. "Just like his father." Then she looked at Henrietta speculatively before she left them.

"Who'd think he'd turn out so nice!" Rachel said over her shoulder. She stood at the parlor window watching Joe down the street.

Henrietta couldn't help giving a little sniff. "He really hasn't changed so much."

"He talks a lot."

"That doesn't make him exactly brilliant."

Rachel turned to look at her.

"He's not really a *thinker*." Henrietta heard herself talking loudly. He hadn't really taken her article seriously. "He says things just to be funny. He thinks he's smart when he's funny!"

Rachel let the lace curtain fall back into place. "But I'm glad Papa asked him to come again, aren't you?"

But Henrietta wasn't at all sure. She didn't answer.

3

"Miss" Henrietta

The Misses Adams sat in their school parlor nodding their heads at Henrietta.

Papa would have called them Southern gentlewomen, the kind that were as out-of-date as the old slave block still standing on the corner of Eutaw Street — except that he could never be purposely unkind. And Papa, least of all, would think it strange that the daughter of a Rabbi was being hired to teach in the Misses Adams' School.

Henrietta smiled.

She sat facing the Misses Adams, who were ranged side by side on their horsehair sofa. She wondered if she would remember how to tell Miss Ada, Miss Loulie and Miss Charlotte apart. All three faces were long and thin, with the same austere expression.

Studying them, Henrietta couldn't help think of the Gothic windows on the Lutheran Church in the neighborhood.

Miss Loulie bent toward her. "I must say we are impressed with your obvious pedagogic attitude."

"A very fine record," Miss Charlotte nodded.

And Miss Ada added generously, "We are indeed fortunate to secure such a scholar for a teacher."

The praise made Henrietta feel uncomfortable. She did not consider herself a scholar, though she knew German well, was reasonably adept at French, and certainly could teach mathematics as well as the teacher who had taught her. He was no scholar at all.

She ducked her head and then brought it quickly back up again. But her discomfort only seemed to make them more pleased with her.

She was full of excitement as she hurried homeward.

Though she couldn't go to Vassar she could go on learning. Papa's study was filled with books and his head with knowledge. She would study and read and write — and at the same time she would teach.

She was a teacher! Papa would be pleased.

She wondered what Joe would say. Henrietta turned her head and grinned her grin into the street. Mr. Exel went by in his butcher wagon and waved at her. Henrietta waved back, grinning some more, and hurried along to Lombard Street.

All the houses on Lombard Street were of red brick, and almost all had the same scrubbed, white marble steps leading up to the front door with a fan-shaped transom above.

When they had come to live there, Mrs. Olive Reeder had peered out at them from behind the Belgian lace curtains of her front windows. They had all jumped out of the wagon carrying something. Mama was following the van in a carriage.

"Where's Papa?" she had cried as she got out. "Where's Papa?"

The driver hastily pulled at his horses and looked behind him. There were rolls of rugs; clothes hampers piled high with kitchen utensils; round wooden laundry tubs packed with china; furniture, bags and boxes and little girls — but no Papa.

Mama rushed into the house. She sent Sadie up to the third floor to look and Rachel down to the cellar. But it was Henrietta who found him. She found Rabbi Szold in the tiny back yard. He was in his shirt sleeves, on his hands and knees, planting a grape vine and a young fig tree.

"And they shall sit, every man under his vine and under his fig tree, and none shall make them afraid."

Her father had raised his head and said the words

very solemnly and loudly to them all, just as if he were standing before his congregation in the synagogue. Henrietta hadn't thought much about the words then, although she knew them. They were just something from the Bible. Her father was always quoting to them from the Bible. Maybe because he was a Rabbi.

Elizabeth Burkley hadn't even known what a Rabbi was.

"You mean he's a Jewish minister?" she had asked.

And Henrietta had laughed. There was no such thing as a Jewish minister. Minister was a Christian word. Carefully she explained this.

She had always been more careful to explain things to the girls at school than to her sisters at home. But there was something she didn't know exactly how to explain. Once when Elizabeth had come home with her, she had tried.

They were in Papa's study.

Elizabeth turned from the big desk and the little white marble busts on the mantel to the books on the wall. The shelves held Hebrew prayer books and scholarly tomes in German as well as in English. Elizabeth looked curiously at the bindings. "It's a beautiful library," she said politely.

"They're just books." Henrietta offhandedly

matched her tone. "They're mostly my father's."

"You mean your father really *reads* them?"

Henrietta glanced quickly at her schoolmate. It was a stupid question, she thought.

"Of course."

"But they're not even in English!" Elizabeth's voice held a sense of shock.

"Not everybody in Baltimore is English."

"My parents are." Elizabeth was proud. "My mother says we're English through and through."

Henrietta looked at her friend. She didn't look any different from anyone else. "My mother's Hungarian. Mr. Exel is German. Our laundress is African, I guess — at least she's a Negro. What difference does that make?"

Elizabeth sniffed. "Well, I wouldn't exactly use a laundress as an equal comparison."

"My father would." Henrietta's voice rang loud. Elizabeth stepped back.

"My father says people are the same whatever they are."

Elizabeth gave a little laugh. "But some people —" She didn't go on to finish. She gave a careful social smile — the kind of smile the ladies of the congregation gave to each other sometimes when they were feeling, but didn't want to admit to, a superiority.

But Elizabeth and she had gone on being friends

— school friends. Things like that were never discussed at school.

And none shall make them afraid. The words came joggling into her thoughts, loudly, the way her father had said them. Henrietta felt a little startled. For it wasn't what she had thought she was thinking about. She listened to the words humming inside her. But what it was she was also trying to hear she could not exactly say. Henrietta reached her house and gazed thoughtfully up at it. Then she ran up the steps.

The hallway was long and narrow with a steep stairway going up. A string of buttons stretched down the length of one wall from front door to the rear. Henrietta had started it, but it was Sadie who had collected most of the buttons. The touch button was Sadie's idea too. It was a button with a bluebird embossed in its glassy top. Anyone who touched the touch button had to forfeit a button to add to the string. Elizabeth had said it was a strange place for a string of buttons.

As Henrietta closed the door, her mother's cheerful tones came indistinctly from the kitchen in the back.

For a moment, Henrietta stood still, listening. Outside, the houses on Lombard Street were exactly the same. But inside, this house was different from all the others.

Henrietta raised her head and sniffed. As if she could catch the difference with her nose. All she smelled was freshly baked cinnamon cake.

Rachel came running down the stairs. "Where have you been?" she demanded.

But Henrietta didn't say. She wanted to save her news to tell Papa first.

"Joe Jastrow was here. With a friend. He was sorry to miss you."

"I'm sorry to miss him too." Henrietta couldn't help smiling a little, thinking of what her father would say when she told him of the Misses Adams hiring her to be a teacher in their school.

"Well, he missed you." Rachel regarded Henrietta meaningfully.

Henrietta smiled broadly. Rachel had a new strange kind of myopia, Henrietta would tell her father. Rachel saw *two's* wherever she looked.

Papa would laugh softly, appreciatively. She could hear it now. It was hard not to compare Joe's bumptious kind of humor to her father's gentle wit.

"Mathematics," she announced at the dining room table. "And English."

Sadie raised her head. "And Hebrew too."

"What would the girls at the Misses Adams' School want with Hebrew!" said Rachel.

Sadie looked surprised.

"They're not Jewish girls," Mama explained.

"I'll be teaching Hebrew at Papa's synagogue," Henrietta said.

"I thought everyone learned Hebrew." Sadie was still puzzled.

"Everyone who is Rabbi Szold's daughter," Rachel said.

Bertha giggled. "That's me!"

"The important thing is that she is teaching," Papa said.

"And whatever Henrietta teaches, she will teach well." Mama gave a cheerful nod of her head.

Henrietta felt a glow of satisfaction.

"Except singing." Rachel grinned at her.

"Well they didn't ask me to teach singing," Henrietta said dryly.

Bertha was staring at Henrietta with undiminished awe. Bertha's eyes, like Mama's, were round and milky blue.

Maggie came in to remove the soup plates and Mrs. Szold began to serve.

"So much depends on the teacher." Rabbi Szold was thoughtful. He seemed not to have heard Rachel's interruption. He had his elbows on the table and his hands folded and he was staring at the bowl of fruit in the center.

"In the Talmud it says that the fault of not learning lies not with the pupil but with the teacher."

Some Rabbis kept their best sermons for their congregations, Henrietta was thinking. But not Rabbi Szold. Religion was a way of life, to be lived every day. To him it all fitted in. The Talmud was a book of wisdom that had taken hundreds of years to write. In it were the thoughts of many great Rabbis.

Would a different teacher have taught her to sing? Henrietta wondered. She would take singing lessons, some day, and see, she promised herself.

Henrietta smiled at her father. It often seemed to her that no one but she was ever really aware of the food for thought that accompanied the meals Mrs. Szold dished out to her family.

Bertha smiled also. "When I grow up I'm going to be a teacher, too."

"Only a little while ago you were going to be a writer," Rachel said.

Bertha looked bewildered.

Henrietta picked up the spoon that Adele had thrown to the floor. She took time to smile at Bertha.

Sadie said, "You only want to be a writer because you want to be like Henrietta."

Sadie wrote poems in secret, and she drew pictures too, that were clearly her own. Sadie had never wanted to be like anyone but Sadie.

"It is fine that Bertha wants to be like Henrietta," Mrs. Szold said.

"And like Mama too," Bertha said warmly and sweetly.

Rachel gave a shout of laughter. But Henrietta hastened to say, "You are like Mama, exactly."

Papa nodded and smiled.

"*Miss Henrietta*," Sadie said in wonder.

Henrietta nodded. That's what the girls at the Misses Adams' School would call her — even if some of them were almost as old as she.

"The rolled cabbage is very good tonight," Mama said with the same degree of satisfaction as she had accepted Henrietta's announcement of her new position.

Rabbi Szold looked at his wife with admiring warmness. "And when is it not good?"

Henrietta sniffed at the succulent dish. Suddenly she was very hungry. *Miss* Henrietta. She smiled as she ate. She really felt much older than seventeen, she decided, and pushed her long hair back off her shoulder, up, like Mama's.

Rachel gazed at her. "You'd better wear it up, too," she advised.

Unaccountably Henrietta was embarrassed. "I don't suppose it will really make any difference."

"It will make a difference to Harry," Sadie said promptly. Harry Friedenwald was nearer Sadie's age than Henrietta's. He lived on the next block. "He'll think you're too old to collect stamps with him anymore."

"I guess it won't make any difference to Joe either." Rachel sighed a little.

"I'm going to be much too busy teaching to even think about Harry or Joe," Henrietta said firmly.

"I have no doubt you will be," her father nodded at her proudly.

It was a compliment, and her mother thought so too. But Rachel was looking at her with an odd expression on her face. And Henrietta pretended not to see.

4
Too Busy

Rachel *turned* around on the piano stool and sighed. "Joe is going home to Philadelphia for the Christmas holidays."

"That'll be a relief." It would give her some time for uninterrupted work, Henrietta was thinking. She frowned at the pile of papers before her to be corrected. Lately the big family living room on the second floor seemed always to be filled with Joe and his friends. Joe came the most often, though. He played chess with Bertha, and talked seriously with Sadie. He teased Rachel, and provoked Henrietta into long discussions. Henrietta smiled, in spite of herself.

Rachel's hands came down loudly, discordantly, on the piano keys. Henrietta looked up to see Rachel glowering at her. Henrietta shrugged and turned back to her work.

Her desk, small and neat, with many little pigeon holes under its hinged top, stood near the three front windows overlooking Lombard Street. Pots of geraniums and begonias filled the wide sills. Mama always watered the plants herself, just as she always ironed Papa's white linen neckbow, although Maggie or Lizzie or Henrietta could have done it just as well. Mama considered doing these things not a duty, but her right and privilege.

Henrietta picked up her pen. She not only had an article to write but much work ahead in preparing lessons for her pupils at the Misses Adams' School. Thinking about the lessons, she frowned.

The Misses Adams judged their pupils' abilities by the amount of information they could recite back. The Misses Adams tested by asking questions, and the pupils demonstrated by giving answers. There must be only one correct answer, Miss Charlotte believed, and that was the one the pupils were taught to give.

"Henrietta! Are you listening?"

Henrietta didn't bother to raise her head. "Are you saying anything?"

Rachel laughed.

Henrietta turned to look at her. She was wearing her new dress. Mama had had it made for her, for Hanukah, Mama said.

"It's a very pretty dress," Henrietta took time to say. "Everyone will be admiring you."

Rachel made a little face. "Papa didn't even notice it."

"Well, he admires you whatever you wear!"

"Not the way he admires you," Rachel said a little enviously. "Just yesterday he was telling some of the members of his congregation about your articles. He acted almost as if they were *his* ideas."

Henrietta grinned. "Well, I guess they are mostly. Sometimes I don't know where his ideas leave off and mine begin."

"Oh, but they were yours! Papa would never have the nerve to say right out what you say when you sign *Sulamith.*"

Henrietta gave a short laugh, but Rachel was busy adjusting the fold of her skirt. She wondered whether Rachel was right. Would she be writing exactly the same opinions in the same way if she were signing Henrietta Szold and not the pen name *Sulamith?* It wasn't an easy question to answer. She thought about it honestly.

"Yes!" she said firmly. "I'm sure I would!"

"Of course you would." The words were an automatic echo, for Rachel was intent on retying the bow in her hair.

Henrietta looked at her sister a little impatiently.

"You remind me of Agatha Porter."

"Who?" Now she had Rachel's attention.

"One of my pupils at the Misses Adams' school. She's the one who knows all the answers to all the questions."

"Well, what's wrong with that?"

"She knows the answers, but not the questions."

Rachel said, "Sometimes what you say doesn't make any sense to me at all."

Henrietta turned back to her desk. But she was still thinking about Agatha. The trouble was, Agatha hadn't learned how to think. For that, it was necessary to consider both the question and the answer.

She looked out the window. The big bay windows on Lombard Street, except for the Jewish houses, were alight with Christmas trees. Henrietta remembered how surprised Elizabeth had been that Jewish families didn't celebrate Christmas.

"It's because we don't believe in Christmas," Henrietta told her.

Elizabeth was aghast. "You mean you don't celebrate anything at all?"

"Well, we have Hanukah," she had been quick to add. "But it isn't anything like Christmas. Except that it comes about the same time. It has an entirely different meaning, though."

She had tried to tell Elizabeth the story of Judah

Maccabee and King Antiochus and the fight for freedom to worship God instead of the king's idols. But she had been a little wary about talking of *freedom* to Elizabeth. Elizabeth's parents didn't believe in exactly the same kind of freedom that her parents did.

Rabbi Szold believed in freedom not only for himself but for everybody else too. As a student in Vienna, he had fought for freedom in the revolution of 1848. And when Abraham Lincoln died, Papa had marched in the funeral procession with tears running down his face. Henrietta thought she remembered. She was five years old.

Freedom to Papa wasn't something you preached about; it was something you did. Like the time he resigned from the Baltimore Minister's Association because they had refused to accept a Negro pastor, although other religious leaders were welcome.

Like Papa, Henrietta felt sharply critical of the Jewish families who celebrated Hanukah as if it were a "Jewish" Christmas.

"We're having turkey!" Bertha announced from the living-room door.

Carefully, Henrietta closed her desk.

Mama carved. Papa always liked to watch her.

"The chicken is very good as usual," Papa said.

"It's not chicken," said Mama. "It is turkey."

"By whatever name, it is good." Papa went on eating.

"Rebecca's name isn't Rebecca anymore," Bertha announced. She was pleased when everyone looked at her.

Mama passed the vegetables. "Is it Becky, then?"

Bertha shook her head. "It's Renée!"

Rabbi Szold dropped his napkin.

"And I suppose the Christmas tree they had was a Hanukah bush." Henrietta didn't smile.

Bertha's eyes grew round. "How did you know?"

"Because your big sister wrote all about it in her newspaper column," Rachel informed her.

"About Rebecca!" It was a cry of anguish.

"Not Rebecca exactly," Henrietta put in quickly.

"People like that," Sadie said.

"People who don't know what's right," Mrs. Szold said emphatically.

Mildly Rabbi Szold said, "Some people try to run away from themselves."

Bertha opened her eyes wide. "How do they do that?"

"They think it's more important to be like somebody else than to be themselves," Sadie said wisely.

Bertha looked puzzled.

Rabbi Szold leaned his elbows on the table and

smiled gently at Bertha. "Once there was a silly man named Shusha who wanted to be like the man who lived next door. So for breakfast he ate just what his neighbor liked, and for dinner he drank just what his neighbor drank, and instead of keeping his own Sabbath he kept the Sabbath which the man next door celebrated. And he lived all his life trying to be like his neighbor, Morris."

"Then what happened?"

"When he had breathed his last breath, and prayed his last prayer, he got ready to go to heaven. And do you know what God said when he got there?"

"Do I have to guess?" Bertha almost held her breath.

"I'll tell you. God did not say, 'Shusha, why were you not Morris?' He said, very sadly, 'Shusha, why were you not Shusha?' "

"Oh," Bertha looked slowly around the table and her glance came to rest on Henrietta. "Poor Rebecca! God won't even speak to her at all." And she burst into tears.

Henrietta rushed around the table, but Papa reached Bertha first. He swung her up in his arms and pressed her head against his shoulder. He carried her out, laughing gently to himself.

It was an old tale Papa had told, but he had made

it simpler for Bertha. The meaning was there though. The exact meaning.

"If you'd sit down, you could pass me some more turkey," Rachel suggested.

But Henrietta stood there for a long moment looking thoughtfully after her father.

5

A Letter Is Talk

Henrietta's nose twitched as she entered a classroom in the Misses Adams' School for Young Ladies. The smell of dried rose petals came to her nostrils. Attar of Roses was Miss Charlotte's favorite scent. The three sisters probably all used the same bottle for economy's sake, Henrietta thought. She went quickly to the window.

The Misses Adams' School looked out upon West Madison Street. The handsome red brick building had a black door and black shutters. The high and narrow windows were kept closed all the time. Henrietta struggled with the catch. Then she leaned far out the window to take a long gulp of air.

"Miss Henrietta!"

Henrietta pulled in her head.

Miss Charlotte hurried across the room. "We never open the window in here!" Her usually gentle voice was mildly chiding, as if it was Henrietta's youth that was at fault, not her upbringing.

Henrietta made a face as the window banged shut before the fragrance had drifted out.

"I came in to commend you for your work, but I had no idea — "

Henrietta looked helplessly at the door. The small girls were already beginning to arrive. Kate would probably spend the morning sneezing; Mary would yawn in great stretching O's, and Bessie would become red and giggly. Henrietta said firmly, "I have meant to talk to you about the work."

Miss Charlotte said hastily, "We are very happy with your work. Very happy indeed. As a matter of fact, we have decided to ask you to teach Miss Ada's French class too, temporarily that is. You do handle the girls so well."

Henrietta felt pleased, though she knew as well as Miss Charlotte that the request was not temporary at all and that it included no advance in pay. She nodded and smiled to show she didn't mind a bit. "But I do want to talk with you a few moments," Henrietta said.

Miss Charlotte put her head on one side,. like a worried wren, and promised to make a moment for her later.

Valiantly, then, Henrietta marched to the window,

opened it for a few moments and closed it again before she began the lesson.

"Today we're going to learn the art of letter-writing."

She set them to work. "Compose a letter to a friend thanking him for a bouquet of — " her nose twitched a little — "red roses."

Agatha giggled. Kate bent her head over her paper and began to scribble furiously with her pen point. Bessie only stared at her blank sheet with a puzzled air, and Mary began to make a meal out of the end of her pen holder.

"I can't think how to start," Bessie said a few moments later. Her paper was blank.

Agatha waved her arm wildly. "I've finished!"

Henrietta sat back. "All right, Agatha. Let us hear how you would begin to write your letter. Perhaps all of us would be better prepared, then, to make a beginning."

Agatha stood up. She cleared her throat.

> Esteemed Sir:
> I have the honor to acknowledge the receipt of your gracious bouquet which I accept with sentiments of respect and consideration.

Agatha gazed at Henrietta proudly. "Of course, it's not the same as writing a *real* letter. It's harder to write when it's not real," she said, not at all modestly.

Henrietta stood up straight. She frowned a little. "A fictitious letter should have exactly the tone and color of a genuine one. A letter should be what you would say to your correspondent if you were with him."

Agatha looked puzzled. The other girls seemed mystified. Henrietta had an inspiration.

"Now, Agatha, suppose you were a young lady *saying* thank you to a gentleman for giving you a beautiful bouquet of roses. Stand up here, and, Bessie, you be the gentleman."

The girls all wriggled and grinned as the two came to the front of the room.

"Now, Agatha, George has just presented you with the flowers. What would you say to tell him you are pleased with them?"

The girls in their seats leaned forward eagerly to watch.

"Here," Henrietta said to Agatha. She took a ruler off the desk. "Pretend this is the bouquet."

Agatha took the ruler and looked blankly at it.

"Do you think it's pretty?" Henrietta prodded.

"It's very pretty," Agatha said dutifully. She regarded the ruler. "How did you know red was my favorite color?"

"Bravo!" said Henrietta, whirling around, and the students laughed at her eager enthusiasm.

She clapped her hands. "Now! Go sit down and *talk* on paper, instead of with your lips! Remember this — a letter is always talk."

All the girls began to write busily.

Henrietta sat at her desk and smiled to herself. Agatha's hand began to wave in the air.

"Yes, Agatha."

Agatha stood up. "I just thought I ought to tell you that *my* letter started out exactly the way Miss Ada said has been proper ever since she was a girl." She sat down.

"Things change," Henrietta said gently. "Every day. Just reading the happenings in the newspaper shows you that."

The girls regarded her blankly.

"Don't you ever read the newspaper?"

Almost all shook their heads. Agatha half giggled, as if Henrietta had suggested something improper. Henrietta sighed.

The girls in the Misses Adams' School, Henrietta thought, were almost all like Agatha.

"Of course they are, dear," Miss Loulie said happily a little later. "Perfect little ladies."

Henrietta nodded, although that wasn't what she

meant. What she meant was, they couldn't think for themselves.

It wasn't easy to make changes with the Misses Adams. They didn't believe in changes. Sometimes, Henrietta suspected, they looked back upon their Southern girlhood with more than nostalgia and used their memories as a guide in the schooling of their pupils.

"We educate our young women to be ladies." Miss Loulie's satisfaction was reflected in the faces of Miss Charlotte and Miss Ada.

"But isn't it important to teach them how to think?"

The Misses Adams looked at each other. Then they all smiled gently at Henrietta, while Miss Charlotte answered.

"I'm afraid we'd lose half our pupils if we tried to teach our young ladies to *compete* with men."

Henrietta sat up very stiffly. "But there's nothing unladylike in learning how to *think*."

Miss Loulie looked a little bewildered.

Miss Ada leaned forward. "What is it you want to do exactly?"

Henrietta took a deep breath. The school's smell of roses seemed always mingled with a peculiar mustiness which persisted no matter how wide she threw open the shutters in her classrooms. Her nose twitched.

"I want to include the study of how to read the newspaper. I would like to add a news class and the reading of a weekly newspaper . . ."

Miss Loulie smiled. But Miss Ada, her voice tremulous, asked, "What else?"

Henrietta looked at them. There was much else, but she said only, "That's all."

Miss Charlotte heaved a sigh. "I think that would be acceptable," she said. And Miss Loulie and Miss Ada also nodded.

Henrietta nodded too. Firmly. It was a start — a very little start. She felt a flutter of excitement at the work ahead of her.

She grinned. Agatha Porter didn't know it, but she would soon learn how to think!

6

Too Smart

"*Next year* in Jerusalem!"

Papa's strong voice led everybody in the toast that always ended the Passover dinner in every Jewish family.

Passover celebrated the Exodus from Egypt when Moses led his people out of slavery. It was all about freedom. To Henrietta it was the best holiday because it was a family celebration. The house on Lombard Street bustled with preparations for weeks ahead. Spring cleaning was always done just before Passover. Curtains were washed, floors waxed and furniture polished. The kitchen was turned inside out, and special dishes, used only on Passover, were taken off their storage shelf. During the eight days of the holiday, *matzo* was eaten instead of bread. Because that is what the Children of Israel ate when they fled into the wilderness.

"Are we going to Jerusalem next year?" Bertha said.

Papa smiled. Everyone knew of course that they would all be in Baltimore next year.

"Not really," Henrietta tried to explain. "Jews everywhere in the world say 'Next year in Jerusalem' on Passover. It means that no matter where Jews live, they always remember their homeland was Jerusalem. It was their country long ago. That's where their beautiful temple once was, and every year they hope that the next year it will be theirs once more."

"Well, it's not likely to be next year." Mama sighed. Mama always sighed when she talked of Jerusalem. Henrietta suspected it was inherited. Her grandmother Schaar must have sighed in exactly the same way, and her mother before her.

"For two thousand years, Jews have hoped to go back to Jerusalem," Rabbi Szold said. "And unfortunately it looks as if that is exactly what our people will have to do."

Rachel raised her head. "You mean that would be bad?"

Thoughtfully Rabbi Szold looked around the table. "Not bad exactly. But sometimes I wonder if there was not some divine Providence that scattered the Jewish people all over the world. Do you think perhaps it was to keep reminding the whole human race how necessary it is to have religious freedom for everyone?"

Henrietta thought about it, though it was not a question her father expected anyone to answer for certain. It was like many of his dinner-table questions. How carefully should the Sabbath be kept in a country where Saturday was a day of work for others? Was God a person or an idea? What was a Jew — a member of a people or of a religion? The question usually started a debate in which even Bertha had her say. But Henrietta suspected that it was the questions that were important, not the answers.

She considered Papa's Passover question. It was another that could not be answered exactly, she thought, and then wondered if perhaps it could.

Sunday afternoon, working at her desk in the upstairs living room, she tried to answer it herself.

And when Joe and his friend Cyrus Adler came in for a Sunday evening visit, Henrietta, flushed with the intensity of her writing, presented Papa's question to them.

It was Joe who argued longest and most loudly, but Henrietta plucked at every point he presented. Now she knew how she felt about the Jews making a country for themselves again, and she felt no hesitancy about proving her point.

She took Papa's question and made it into a statement. The Jews, because they were God's people, didn't need a country of their own.

"But look how many times they've been kicked out of other countries!" Joe began ticking them off on his blunt fingertips. "Two thousand years ago they were destroyed as a nation in Palestine. They went to live in other countries. But because they were Jews, with a different religion, they were expelled from England in the thirteenth century, from France in the fourteenth, from Spain in the fifteenth century . . ."

"That's exactly the point!" Henrietta pounced on that. "We are not living in the thirteenth, the fourteenth or the fifteenth centuries. This is the nineteenth century. In today's enlightened world, religion is a personal matter. Our home as Jews is anywhere on the whole earth, in every land of our birth or our adoption. And that, I believe, is the way it was meant to be. Today as Jews we are Germans in Germany, Frenchmen in France, Englishmen in England and Americans in America! We are at home everywhere!"

"Rot!" said Joe.

Rachel, sitting beside him, gasped.

Joe took time to say, "Pardon me," and then went over to sit next to Henrietta.

"Jews are not Americans in America so long as a hotel puts out a 'No Vacancy' sign to any Jew who wants to stay there!"

"When was that?" Rachel said.

Cyrus said, "In New York, not too long ago. There was a big hullabaloo."

Henrietta remembered it very well. She had even written an article on it for the *Jewish Messenger*.

Joe said, "I say — when Jews all over the world say 'Next year in Jerusalem' at Passover, there are still some good reasons for making the wish."

But Henrietta could not be downed. "You can't blame a whole nation for the stupidity of one hotel manager. I didn't say that all Jews are perfect beings either. Some do as many stupid things as some Christians."

Her voice rang out confidently.

"All I can point out is that the American Jewish people have among them some wealthy leaders. If the Jews in our country had wanted the words 'Next year in Jerusalem' to be more than a gesture, why have they not supported their faith and shown their social responsibility and exercised their generosity and imagination by buying back the land that was once theirs?"

Joe stood up; he waved his arms around. He almost shouted — "The answer is — why should they! As Americans, our constitution grants us the freedom to worship as we want!"

Henrietta folded her hands in her lap and smiled.

"Exactly," she said softly. "That is my point exactly! There is absolutely no need for Jews to have a country of their own. 'Next year in Jerusalem' is only a gesture."

Joe opened his mouth a time or two, fiddled with his mustache and glowered at her.

Henrietta turned her back, glowing with her victory.

But as soon as the boys had left, Rachel whirled upon her.

"Do you always have to win every argument?"

Henrietta opened her eyes wide. "We were just having a little discussion."

Rachel snorted. "Every time you discuss something with boys you have to show them how smart you are!"

Smart. Henrietta winced.

"You're wrong!" she threw out blindly. But Rachel was running up the stairs.

Slowly Henrietta followed. But instead of going

up the steep stairway to the bedroom they shared on the third floor, she stopped on the second and went down the hall to the sitting room.

She frowned at the rosewood square piano where she and Rachel vied with each other in pounding out duets, the cheery fireplace with its gas logs, and Mama's potted geraniums and begonias on the wide sills. She looked for a long time at her desk before she sat down and took up her work.

Later, they undressed without speaking in their third-floor front bedroom. In the silence, Sadie could be heard mumbling in her sleep in the smaller middle room in which she slept by herself, and though it was late, Adele was still scolding in her crib in the back bedroom which she shared with the sound sleeper, Bertha. Rachel closed the bedroom door, opened the window, and without saying good night, got into bed.

Henrietta picked up her hairbrush. Though it was night and not morning, she slowly began to brush her hair. Her hair was not as thick as Rachel's. It was darker and too fine. Methodically Henrietta counted to a hundred before she set her brush down. Rachel turned over in bed.

Henrietta looked at her top bureau drawer. It was a jumble. It was always rumpled when Rachel dug into it to borrow a ribbon or a handkerchief. Henrietta hesitated a moment before she closed the drawer. She would set it straight in the morning. She got into bed and closed her eyes. But she did not sleep. In her mind she carefully set her bureau drawer to rights. The belts here, and the ribbons there, the handkerchiefs in one pile and the scarfs in another. But the mental exercise did not bring her any closer to sleep.

She listened to the clank of freight trains lumbering down Pratt Street past the Baltimore and Ohio machine shops only a block away. Then she strained her ears to hear the tooting of the vessels in the distant harbor.

Henrietta flung over. Rachel was asleep. Soundly asleep. Henrietta stared at her.

She thought of Joe arguing hotly, his round face pink, his usual admiring glance changed to one of helpless anger.

Victory? She knew somehow, then, it wasn't hers at all.

7

A Handkerchief

Papa took Henrietta with him on his trip to Europe. Mama decided. She had gone on a visit to her family a few years before, and Henrietta stayed home to take care of Papa. Now it was time for Papa to go. And Henrietta went with him.

"I'm green with envy!" Rachel said extravagantly, and to prove it, she sat around strumming mournful songs on the guitar that Joe had encouraged her to try. Mama ignored her, and Papa was too busy to notice, but Henrietta suspected she was not really sorry about not going.

At night Rachel turned her back and promptly closed her eyes without even talking about it. Henrietta pretended not to notice.

They sailed the second week of June. Papa stood at the rail waving at Mama, and he continued waving long after they saw only specks in the distance.

Henrietta laughed at him. "But you can't see her any more!"

"Not with my eyes perhaps," Papa said, his arms still moving slowly.

Suddenly Henrietta felt guilty. Mama should have come with Papa, not her.

"Mama does not need to go," Papa said simply. "We already regret that you never knew your Grandmother Schaar." Papa took out his handkerchief and wiped his eyes.

Henrietta thought of the picture hanging over Papa's desk in his study. In it her grandmother wore a bonnet tied under her chin. Remembering the bow, Henrietta smiled.

"I always tell your mother I fell in love with her mother before I fell in love with her. It was the truth too."

It was a family joke.

"She was the only one who didn't feed me lentils," Papa said.

Henrietta grinned. This was a story Papa told over and over again, and she listened to it once more as they walked along the deck together.

There were sixteen other cabin passengers. She nodded to one and then another shyly as Papa talked about his boyhood days.

Since his parents were dead, he was brought up by uncles, and while going on with his studies in Pressburg was boarded out to families, a different one each day in the week. Each good housewife, wanting to feed the student well, gave him lentils for dinner. Every time Papa told the story he made a face at the memory all over again.

"Will we go to Pressburg?"

"Yes, we will go to Pressburg," Papa said with a sigh.

But first they would go to see Mama's relatives.

Mama had been born in the village of Cziffer in Slovakia, one of twelve children. The family owned a prosperous farm and brewery, and her mother had been a good manager. She was such a good manager that when the father died she was able to continue successfully.

She solved the problem of educating so many children by starting a school in her own home, to which the neighbors' children came also. It was as an instructor in this home school that the young Benjamin Szold came to the Schaar household.

The lonely young man fell in love with the entire family. He couldn't remember his own mother, and ever afterward he looked upon the head of this large and happy group as his mother too. When he took the youngest girl as his bride, he carried her mother's picture with him also, and it had been hanging over his desk in his study for as long as Henrietta could remember.

Henrietta's Grandmother Schaar had died the year before. Papa was coming himself to be present at the laying of the headstone on her grave.

Listening to Papa, Henrietta looked around. One family in particular among the other passengers interested her. There were two girls, one younger like Rachel, the other nearer her own age. Both smiled at her as they strolled together, following their parents.

Papa settled himself into a deck chair, and Henrietta sat down too. Papa closed his eyes.

But Henrietta did not feel like a nap. She jumped up and went to the rail. Throwing her head back, she let the fresh breeze push against her forehead. The two girls came around the deck together, and stopped to smile at her.

"I'm Theresa Albright," one said.

"I'm Mary," said her sister.

They were friends immediately. Arm in arm, with Henrietta in the middle, they walked briskly along the deck. Papa opened his eyes, one time round, and smiled before he closed them again. When they passed Mr. and Mrs. Albright, the girls' mother put on her glasses, examined Henrietta closely, and gave a nod. Henrietta had to giggle at this visible sign of approval.

She sat down with them, feeling comfortable with all the chatter.

"You be careful, young lady, or these two will talk an arm and a leg off you." Mr. Albright gave them only momentary attention.

"Oh, I'm used to that!" Henrietta said quickly. "I have four sisters."

"Imagine having four like Theresa!" Mary said.

Mrs. Albright looked curiously at Henrietta. For some reason, Henrietta felt herself flushing a little, almost as if she were talking to company in her mother's parlor. She had to smile at herself. Mrs. Albright wasn't a bit like the ladies of Papa's congregation. She was — Henrietta looked at her thoughtfully. She couldn't exactly put her finger on what the difference was.

"Who are you traveling with?" Mrs. Albright asked.

"My father." Henrietta nodded toward the distant chair.

Mrs. Albright put on her glasses again to regard the sleeping figure.

Even asleep, Henrietta thought proudly, Papa looked elegant.

"Papa is a Rabbi." It came out with pride.

"A what?" Mary said.

Mrs. Albright had raised herself sharply.

"You mean you are *Jewish!*"

Henrietta looked at her in surprise. The word had an odd sound on Mrs. Albright's lips — as if it weren't quite nice.

Unaccountably Henrietta straightened her shoulders.

Mrs. Albright fumbled a moment with the contents of her bag. "I've forgotten my handkerchief!" she said. "Mary, will you run down to my stateroom and get one for me?"

"You can use mine, Mother," Theresa held out a neatly folded square. "I have a fresh one."

"I didn't ask you for yours," her mother said sharply. "Will you please go with Mary to make sure she finds it. I'm certain Miss — " she didn't bother with the name — "will excuse you."

Henrietta jumped up. "Of course!" She whirled and walked quickly away. Neither of the girls moved. Henrietta held her shoulders up until she was out of sight. Then she went to the railing, and pressed against it until it hurt.

She should be feeling angry, she told herself. At their stupidity. But somehow she only felt sick.

8
"I Belong"

"*Joe brings* Rachel flowers," Sadie said.

"And Mama candy." Bertha giggled.

"He brought Sadie a button."

"We put it on the button string!" Adele shouted.

Bertha looked pained. "But Adele went and swallowed it first."

Henrietta grinned and hugged them all. It was good to be back on Lombard Street.

"Everything is the same," Mama said happily.

But it was not the same, Henrietta could see. Then she wondered whether the change she felt was only in herself.

At first she had tried to keep account of their daily travels in a diary. Conscientiously she had begun by making entries from June 24, when they disembarked at Bremerhaven, until July 3. And then surrounded and almost overwhelmed by the number of relatives, she simply gave up reporting anything but her delight. She counted forty of the family through Hamburg, Berlin, Dresden, Prague and Vienna.

Aunt Pepi, Mama's sister, looked just like Mama. The German cousins teased her about her American accent and laughed at her *r's.* She met her Uncle Heinrich and her Aunt Mina and her charming Uncle Naftali and Papa lost their valises in one place and for a week she had nothing to wear but one dress. She had a wonderful time.

But strangely, what she thought of most often when she was back home on Lombard Street was the sight of the ancient ghetto in Pressburg where Papa had studied and hungered and grown sick of eating lentils.

Papa took her through the narrow twisted streets of the town to this section where Jews had had to live. Long ago there had been iron gates which used to be closed every night. Now, Jews were free to come and go as they wanted, and the iron gates had been removed.

But as Henrietta passed through the gateway into the ghetto street she had feelings she could not immediately name. They were sharp and bitter and not so much sad as angry.

"Your nose twitches sometimes," her cousins had

told her with amusement. "And when you get angry, you grow ten feet tall!"

She must have looked like that even when telling Mama about it, because Bertha, listening with eyes growing wider, suddenly stepped back and began to cry.

Papa explained gently. "A long time ago Jews lived in these ghettos. Because they were Jews, they were not allowed to take part in the life of the city outside the ghetto street, or to own land or do any ordinary kind of business."

Suddenly Papa seemed to be talking only to himself. "Perhaps that is why their books and their learning became so important to them. A man's mind is free in the search for knowledge even though his body is held behind iron gates."

Henrietta listened to Papa with new wonder. She was eager to get to her desk once more; she had many articles to write. All at once she felt close to her European relatives. And somehow also to the Jews who once had lived in that ancient ghetto.

"I belong," she whispered as she hurried up the stairs. Strongly, she felt she belonged to all of them.

Henrietta viewed with surprise the boys who came with Joe to visit the family on Lombard Street. They seemed so young. She was glad when the new term opened at the Misses Adams' School and she was back at her teaching.

She worked hard at it. She was no longer hesitant about tackling the Misses Adams for permission to make changes. Her salary was still the same, but she had reward enough. Her girls were learning how to think! The glow of accomplishment filled Henrietta when Agatha questioned the question and found several ways to answer it.

Henrietta believed wholeheartedly that giving information was only the lesser part of a teacher's work. She believed it most important to train the mind to think for itself, not to stuff it with information as one would a chicken with crumbs. She began to see that what was real was what attracted a child. An event *happening* was history growing. Growth was life! Nimbly she worked to show her young pupils how to recognize this.

She took a flower to school one day, and an insect the next. She took several of the worms for which Papa had paid a penny a hundred to the little girls to remove from his rosebushes. When it rained one day, splashing a spring torrent, she opened the window and caught some drops in the drinking cup. She talked about rain, and led her whole class out one early morning to inpect the dew.

The Misses Adams were perplexed at this activity.

"It's important to teach life," Henrietta explained as clearly as she was able. She felt solemn just speaking of it, and her solemnity in some way must have been imparted to the three timorous ladies. For they did not object.

"Open your eyes to see," she told her young class on the last day of school. "Unplug your ears. Use your nose to smell and your mind to think! Things are happening all around you — every day! Think!"

When the girls crowded around her to say good-by for the summer, she was pleased and happy.

She walked briskly home in the warm spring afternoon smelling the early green of things growing. Henrietta felt as if she herself were still "growing," too, although she was twenty-two years old. Growing toward what? She didn't know. Henrietta gave a little skip as she went down Lombard Street.

She opened the front door softly, pausing, as she always did, to sniff. The wonder of the house was submerged a little under the onslaught of voices coming from the parlor. One of Mama's committee meetings, Henrietta decided, for it was not the Sabbath. She listened a moment.

"It's all well and good to have such a smart girl writing for newspapers and teaching school — but does Henrietta know there are other things in life, too!"

Henrietta stood there, unmoving.

"Have you noticed, Sophie dear," said another voice, "how old-maidish Henrietta acts sometime? Tell me, why with all her amazing qualities and achievements she still has no confidence in herself!"

"Why must she always prove herself against some yardstick of perfection? Why can't she be satisfied to find herself a good husband. Tell me why!"

Henrietta took her hand off the doorknob. Purposefully she removed her coat and laid it on a chair. Then with her shoulders back and her head up, she marched to the half-open door of the parlor and stepped in.

9
Raspberry Syrup

Her mother faced her, imperturbably, from behind the coffee tray. "Come in, Henrietta," she said loudly.

Henrietta was already in.

"We were just talking about you," Mrs. Goldman said, and her cup rattled in its saucer.

"I know." Henrietta accepted a cup and sipped at it. It surprised her to taste tea. Mama was a coffee drinker and that is what she usually served to the ladies. The thought crossed Henrietta's mind that one of them must have asked for tea. She made herself stay there sipping to the last drop before she set the cup down.

She knew that she would never again look at a cup of tea without instant distaste.

She helped her mother carry the tea things back into the kitchen when the ladies had gone, but she didn't say anything. What was there to say?

Her mother didn't say anything either, not immediately, not until the cups and saucers were washed up, and the silver put away. Then she turned about, put her capable hands on Henrietta's shoulders and gave her a gentle little shake. "All they do is *talk, talk, talk*. Such gossips they are!"

Henrietta laughed. But it wasn't a very successful sound.

She rose early, as usual, every summer morning, though she did not have to hurry to school to teach. Before breakfast she took her writing paper and her books out to the small back garden where she sat under the flowering fig tree and worked. Papa was often there too.

He liked to walk up and down in the garden, meditating. Slowly he traversed the tiny paths of gravel in between beds of bright flowers. He often stopped to examine a new bud, or shake his head over a blighted stalk. He usually spent some time twining a wandering shoot of the grapevine around the trellis, and pinching his rosebushes.

Sometimes Adele would dash out of the side door of the house and shriek through the garden with Lizzie just behind.

"Komm, trink dein Milch!" Lizzie would cry after her.

Papa just shook his head and smiled gently. He didn't mind the noise of children. He said it helped him to think.

Papa liked to think out loud. Often he practiced his Saturday morning sermon in the garden.

Henrietta sat listening, although she had intended to write her own article.

"Love it is that makes the term home . . ." he was saying. "Love warms the atmosphere of the house and brightens it. But love must be combined with wisdom . . ."

Henrietta stopped listening and concentrated on her own writing.

It was strange, thought Henrietta, how carefully wrapped up her true feelings always were. She was different from her sisters. Rachel seldom held back. Sadie, though quieter, always looked the way she was feeling even though she usually never bothered to put it into words. Bertha laughed or cried without restraint and without embarrassment. And the noisiest of them all was Adele. She stamped her feet, or screamed with ease.

Only with her words on paper, did Henrietta show her deeper feelings. In her articles her anger showed in sharp little words, and sometimes — Henrietta made a face — in swollen bumps of grandiloquence. Although she was getting better at that, she decided. She was learning to say what she wanted to say without quite so many self-conscious flourishes of phrases.

Henrietta looked at the paper before her. She knew somehow she was not a writer, not really. Not like Louisa May Alcott, or George Eliot. Her mind was too bent on order to allow her hand to be carried away into flights of sentiment or poetry. Her writing was a tool, not an art. She let the paper on her lap fall to the grass and sat there staring at it.

"Adopt a central idea — " Papa had once told her. "Never depart from it, but relate everything to that idea. Great men lived that way. To Moses it was the Law; to Judah Maccabee, right; to Abraham Lincoln, freedom."

"*And none shall make them afraid—*" The rhythm of the words jogged suddenly inside Henrietta. She looked up into the branches of the fig tree with startled eyes.

Papa paused, looking at her curiously.

Henrietta shook her head. "I guess I was only thinking." She picked up her paper, bundled her things together and went into the house.

She met Rachel in the hall. Rachel wore that dreamy look she carried about her for a while after she had taken a short nap. Rachel loved to nap.

Henrietta looked at her a little impatiently. To Henrietta, napping was just a waste of precious time. Rachel yawned and opened the side door to go into the garden.

Sadie and Adele were in the kitchen. Bertha had gone out with Maggie.

"Where's Mama?" Henrietta asked them.

"She's cross!" said Adele happily.

Henrietta frowned, though not at her. "What are you doing?"

"We're testing," Adele said importantly. "We're deciding whose pickles are the best in the whole of Baltimore."

"Of course, we're only testing Mama's." Sadie smiled.

Henrietta felt mystified. "Well then how are you going to tell which is best."

"We're giving Mama first prize anyway, so it won't make any difference." Adele helped herself to another gherkin from the jar.

"But you can't make a test out of just one jar!"

"We're pretending," Sadie said.

"But we're not pretending about the prize." Adele sucked on her pickle reflectively. "We're going to give Mama a real prize."

Mama came in. "What's this about a prize?" She looked tired. She had been up almost since daybreak,

Henrietta knew, to make raspberry syrup from her mother's old recipe, before the day turned hot. The bottles were standing on the kitchen table, a rich ruby color in the sunlight.

"You win!" Adele announced.

"First prize!"

"That's nice." Mama gave them an automatic smile. "Now I'd better take those bottles of raspberry syrup down to the cellar." She counted them. "Thirteen."

"We'll help you. We'll carry them all down for you. That will be your prize." Sadie picked up one and held it to the light admiringly.

There was a crash. Sadie's fingers were still poised in the air, but the bottle was on the floor and the syrup was oozing out. Sadie gasped.

Henrietta glanced at her mother.

"Now we'll only have the trouble to carry twelve jars," Mama said heartily. And with not another word she handed Sadie a second bottle. Henrietta helped. As she carried bottles down, she was thinking that Mama not only knew when to scold, but she knew when not to, too. To Henrietta, that seemed even more important.

10
Some Kind of Magic

"Well, I don't see why she has to scream all the time." Rachel's brown hair had curious blond lights in it when she flung her head in the sunlight, Henrietta thought as she looked up from her work.

"Adele's sick," Henrietta reminded gently.

"And fretful, and cross and bratty and insufferable!" said Rachel with no gentleness at all.

"Having scarlet fever helps. I'd better go up and read to her again for awhile."

"That *Arabian Nights* book of yours is almost falling to pieces you've read from it so much. And if you're thinking of reading some more — don't. I've already tried it. It doesn't work."

Henrietta smiled but didn't say anything. Rachel grew hurried and restless when she read to the little girls.

Rachel looked at Henrietta a little enviously. "How do you get them to stay quiet long enough even to listen?"

"Magic!" said Henrietta. "It's in the book." She closed her desk and stood up.

Rachel eyed her for a few moments. "It's not in the book," she said softly. "I think it's in you."

Henrietta whirled in surprise.

Rachel made a face. "I hate to admit it, of course. But Henrietta, you do have some special magic with those children. This morning I felt Adele's arms around my neck and I said to her, 'You dear!' And you know what she did? She quickly took her arms away and said very coolly — 'Oh, I thought you were Henrietta!' "

Rachel sighed. "Now she says no one is to come near her. Not even Mama. No one but you."

Henrietta sat down in the chair next to Adele's bed. Adele flung out an arm toward her, mumbled and then drifted back to sleep. Henrietta looked at her. Even in sleep, Adele was independent and determined.

Henrietta sat back, remembering another little sister; she had died before Adele was born. Henrietta had been fourteen years old and Joanna three, and because Mama was so busy, Joanna had always been

Henrietta's special charge. Henrietta was ill with a
shaking kind of sickness for a long time after Joanna
died.

There had been two other baby girls in the Szold
family too. Henrietta did not remember the infants at
all. She was two years old when Estella was born, and
barely four at the birth of Rebecca. Neither had lived
more than a few months, and Henrietta had been too
young to know why Mama grieved. Then Rachel was
born, and after her came Sadie, then Bertha, and
Adele.

Mama and Papa considered themselves lucky to
have five healthy, fine girls, but never got over feeling
sad at the three they had lost.

Tenderly, Henrietta touched Adele's cheek and
smoothed the covers around her.

"I'm going to have lots of children," she promised
herself, and went quietly out of the room and down
to the kitchen to help Mama.

Her mother looked up from her ironing when Henrietta came in.

"She's asleep," Henrietta said.

Mama looked at her closely. She finished ironing
the bit of white linen that was Papa's cravat and set
the iron back on the stove.

"So you'll be the one to go to Cincinnati," she announced. "You need the change more than me."

For a moment Henrietta didn't know what Mama was talking about.

"With Papa," Mama said. She meant Papa's invitation to make a speech at the first commencement of the Hebrew Union College there. "You will go too."

"Me?"

Mama was pleased with her decision. "You!"

Papa was pleased, too. Henrietta was on a summer recess from teaching school and she had no excuse to offer. But the summer was unusually hot and Adele fretful. It was decided that Bertha would go with them too. They went to Cincinnati with Papa, and it surprised Henrietta that she had such a good time.

She sat at the head table with Papa and she was pleased and proud at the success of his speech. People really laughed at his jokes, not out of politeness but because his jokes were funny. It was a very grand banquet that followed the commencement exercises. She guessed there were almost five hundred people there.

Afterwards Papa steered her through the crowd carefully.

"There is someone who is very eager to meet you," said Dr. Wise smiling at Henrietta as he stopped Papa. Henrietta stepped back a little.

"I mean *you*, Miss Henrietta. He has been wanting

to meet you ever since he heard you would be accompanying your father."

Henrietta was so surprised she did not even hear his name.

"But you are so young!" the old gentleman said in surprise. "From your articles I took you to be one of much greater years."

That made Henrietta laugh. She laughed a great deal before the evening was over. Total strangers to herself and her father asked to be introduced to her. She was amazed to learn how many people knew of her through her writings. It was almost as if she were a famous writer. She had always thought that people talked about the articles because it pleased her father.

She was invited to tea, and to dinner, and to drive in the country. She would have liked to accept all if there had been time.

Papa was proud at all the attention she was getting. She thought it might have surprised him a little too, because he had not even mentioned her writings. She even wondered if her work might not be pretty good after all. Though she had to honestly admit to herself that nothing she had written had ever been as good as she thought it should be.

Full of excitement, she couldn't sleep, and easing

quietly out of the bed she was sharing with Bertha, she went to write a letter to Baltimore.

Nine-year-old Bertha had had the same idea earlier. Her letter to Mama was on the table waiting for Henrietta to correct and mail for her.

> Yesterday Papa preached a sermon at the Temple and he was introduced as "the Rev. Benjamin Szold of Baltimore, who is distinguished for his wit and wisdom as much as he is loved for his piety and sincerity." I went to Dr. Wise's home afterwards and I had a nice time. I had some apples, pears, and cherries off their trees. There were fifteen or twenty rabbies there. At dinner when we were going to eat the turkey, some more rabbies came in, then everybody got up from the table to talk to the rabbies that came in, then the rabbies that came in took the other people's places and began to eat, and the others went off. Not long after dinner we had ice cream and cake, and then we went home.

Henrietta wrote her own impressions carefully:

> I have been spending a delightful time . . . late hours have taken my appetite away . . . flattery, compliments, and kind words have pleased me. My head has nearly been turned, for I have been treated almost as you read of

talented authoresses being treated, and if I
do not come back conceited and vain, it is my
good strong sense that has saved me, and the
remembrance of Mama and home.

Letters from home reached them promptly. Mama
wrote:

I am so glad that Papa will arrive home soon,
and I hope he will not be too tired from talking so much in Cincinnati. Since Papa has
been away I can see how much people tor-
ment him by asking favors of him, and I
know it makes him feel doubly bad that he
cannot help them financially. Please give Bertha for me a little piece of advice. If she
should again have occasion to go into an orchard, tell her not to eat any apples. Just as
when you go into a wine-cellar where wine is
stored, and you drink wine, you get much
quicker drunk. So in an apple orchard, when
you eat apples there you get much quicker
sick. Henrietta, dear child, please don't laugh
that I who am so prosaic just for once write
poetry, and say something through the mouth
of a poet who can express it better in a few
lines than I could in a whole long letter:

> Mir ist als ob ich die Hande
> auf's Haupt Dir legen sollt'

Betend, dass Gott Dich erhalte
so rein und schoen und hold.*

Feeling like crying, Henrietta opened the other letter. As she read it she saw Rachel, her hair silk in the sunshine, her cheeks round and soft, and smiles in her eyes as well as on her lips.

Joe arrived from Germantown this morning. He needed, he said, a change of surroundings and people to talk to. We read your latest article and thought it very good. Joe says that instead of writing for periodicals you should spend the time writing letters to him. I told him that he is an egotist, and that he is, in the real sense of the word.

Henrietta looked at it a long time before she put it away.

* I feel I should put my hands on your head and pray that God keeps you as sweet as you are.

11

The Pretty One

"*Bugs!*" Miss Yarnell said. Gingerly she crossed the bare floor of the room. She wore her tennis shoes all the time, even in her nightgown.

Wearily, Henrietta sat down in the rocking chair in her room at the Egg Harbor Hotel in Egg Harbor City. With careful patience she looked at the partner she had drawn for the Botany Club weekend.

If Rachel had been here too, they would have laughed at the bugs, and the lumpy mattresses, at the fat proprietor who spoke only German, at the heavy meals and the weightier humor. They would have battled the mosquitoes, the logy weather, the dust and the dirt with sharp giggles. But Miss Yarnell couldn't see anything funny in bugs. To avoid stepping on them she wore her tennis shoes even in the bath.

It was the annual Botany Club outing.

Rachel and Henrietta both had become ardent botanists.

With the other members of the group they often went on a day of collecting and identifying. Sometimes they allowed the little girls to tag along.

All would climb on the electric motor car and ride to the end of the line near Mount Washington. They carried their botany box, a queer-looking affair that often made other riders look at them curiously. They rambled in the woods and fields on the outskirts of the city looking for specimens.

Rachel always giggled when Henrietta talked about her finds as if flowers and plants could feel and almost think. Mama did that too.

Mama's plants were always "happy" when they were well fed and bursting with bloom. The girls walked together on the Botany Club outings. They giggled together more than the others. Henrietta's cry of delight was the loudest of all when a rare find was discovered. Tenderly, she placed it in the specimen box, and when she got home she raced to look it up in the botany book.

Somber Dr. Cuthbert would clear his throat and wink at Rachel when Henrietta excitedly guessed at the classification. Mrs. Ridgley would smile at her as if she were a little girl. They would congratulate

Rachel, too, generously, on any of her finds, but Rachel always credited her successes to Henrietta.

"All I have to do is to keep my eye on Henrietta's nose," she told them blandly.

"Her nose?" Dr. Cuthbert's gentlemanly tones could not conceal his surprise.

Rachel shook her head up and down with a serious air. "It twitches!" she whispered loudly. "Watch it! When I walk with Henrietta, it's just like walking with a divining rod. The moment we come within a find, her nose wiggles."

They all laughed at Rachel's joke, Henrietta, as much as everyone else. But she knew Rachel's words were almost true. For her nose did twitch like a small sensitive wand. Not at flower specimens perhaps — but at fragrances almost undetectable, just as when she was angry her nostrils flared in indication of her feelings.

The two sisters smiled at each other in private understanding. They had always been roommates, sharing bedroom and bureau, but it was only since Rachel had grown up that they had become best friends.

The students who came to the house with Joe often came back to see Rachel. That summer, Joe was spending as many days at the house on Lombard Street as he did in his own home in Philadelphia. He played chess with Bertha, teased Sadie, petted Adele, sang to Rachel's accompaniment on the guitar and asked Henrietta's advice on all manner of things.

Henrietta still argued every point with Joe and won most of them, almost as though she were trying to prove something to Rachel. But Rachel only smiled.

Henrietta, Rachel and Sadie, too, were invited often to the Jastrow house in Philadelphia. A fine warm friendship existed between the two families.

Joe was teaching Rachel how to play tennis, and when he was gone he wrote long letters to every member of the family.

"My dear Henrietta — " he always began. Joe was a brother to them all.

"Wouldn't it have been nice if your sister had come too?" Miss Yarnell said.

"She's spending the weekend in Philadelphia." Henrietta began to wish she had gone to visit the Jastrows too. She had thought it would be a lark to attend the weekend outing of the Botany Club in Egg Harbor City, instead.

Miss Yarnell gave a little shriek and pulled her tennis-shoed feet off the floor. "Bugs!" she said again in tones of grim despair.

Henrietta sighed. The first night, she lay sleepless. She listened to the cry of the whippoorwill, the caw of the crow, the crow of the cock, and the buzzing of the mosquitoes. Her ears picked out the chirping of the birds in the big chestnut tree outside her window, and the audible sleep of her companion in the next bed.

Henrietta spent an exhausting morning in the woods.

"Your sister is younger than you, isn't she?" Miss Yarnell hiked along beside her. She at least was refreshed by her sonorous night, Henrietta reflected.

"Quite a bit."

"My, she's such a pretty girl!"

"A real beauty!" Dr. Cuthbert fell into step beside them. "Isn't it too bad she didn't come too?"

"I miss her," Henrietta admitted

"It's unusual for sisters to be such good friends." Dr. Cuthbert made it a compliment.

"And you're not a bit alike!" Miss Yarnell said chummily.

"Maybe that's why," Henrietta said wryly.

"Oh, I think they are a great deal alike." Dr. Cuthbert talked right over Henrietta's head, as if she weren't there. "Personally, I'd be hard put to choose between them."

Henrietta felt surprised, and Miss Yarnell giggled.

"I think he likes you," she confided to Henrietta a little later.

Though Henrietta didn't mean to, she snorted.

She tried to have a good time, but not even the specimen hunting was really interesting that morning, and it wasn't much better later.

That afternoon, she played awkward tennis with three of the other members in the midday sun.

"There's a letter for you!" Miss Yarnell *yoohooed* out the window as, muscle-sore and weary, Henrietta plodded up the walk.

Perhaps Rachel had changed her mind and was joining them after all. Henrietta dashed up the stairs to see it.

"From Rachel?" Miss Yarnell hovered before her.

Henrietta nodded. She read it quickly.

"She's engaged," Henrietta said and managed a smile very well. Joe had been elected Professor at the University of Wisconsin. It meant they would get married right away.

Calmly, Henrietta put the letter back into the envelope, and the envelope into the dresser drawer.

The dinner gong rang.

"My! I'm starved!" she said.

But sitting in the clattery hotel dining room she couldn't swallow a thing. Halfway through the Hungarian goulash, she burst into tears.

"It's the excitement," Miss Yarnell explained. "Because her sister's engaged."

Solicitously, she helped Henrietta up the stairs and

made her lie down on her bed.

Henrietta's muscles ached, and her head blazed and she wished Miss Yarnell would go away and that she were back home on Lombard Street.

Miss Yarnell sat by her bed and comfortingly patted her shoulder.

"Remember, dear Henrietta, it is almost as sad for us too."

"Sad?"

Henrietta raised her head in surprise.

On Miss Yarnell's face was a doleful expression. "The Botany Club is losing such a useful member," she said. There were tears in her eyes.

Henrietta sat up in bed, shook out her handkerchief, blew her nose — and then laughed.

12

The Russians

In 1889 everyone was talking about the Russians. Baltimore was suddenly full of them. The ladies of the congregation flocked, breathless and eager, to the Szold house. They came with stories of the immigrants. How they were coming in boatloads to escape the persecution of Russia's Czar. They spoke with distaste of the ones they had seen — their ignorance, their common speech and their poverty.

"Some of them can't speak a word of English yet!" Mrs. Goldman's soft chin waggled in consternation.

"They're Russians," Papa said. "In Russia they spoke Russian or Yiddish — they have to learn English."

"Personally, I wouldn't even let my Esther walk through that area," Mrs. Green said. "They're not only uneducated and poor but they're dirty. They smell." Her whole face wrinkled.

"So would you smell if you spent weeks in the hold of a creaking old boat."

Many of the ladies gasped at Henrietta's plain words.

But her father did not admonish her; neither did her mother. That's the way they felt too. The Russians pouring into the United States were Jews like themselves. Less fortunate ones — for they had no money, no homes, no jobs and most of them could not even read or write the English language. "Greenhorns" the ladies called them unkindly; and piously started a collection to help them. But not many opened their doors and their hearts to them as Rabbi Szold did.

"We're nothing but a confessional," Sadie said, when the Russians overflowed their dining-room table night after night.

It would be more appropriate to call us a 'wailing wall,' " Henrietta said. "Like Solomon's temple in Jerusalem."

"What you mean is free boarding house," Bertha said. But willingly she and Sadie and Adele had run up and down the cellar stairs bringing the jams, the jellies, the fruit and the meat that Mama had stored there. It seemed to Henrietta that the cellar became as familiar to her as the living room. Samples from its barrels of pickled meats and shelves of jarred preserves supplemented the table every night. Mama spent her days in the kitchen. It was the only thing she could do for them, she said, and she was determined to do her best.

Rachel and Joe were married and living in Madison, Wisconsin, and though Henrietta missed Rachel, she had no time to think of herself. The writing and teaching went on, but now she put her shyness in her pocket to speak and solicit help and money for the Russians. She could not bear to see a self-satisfied expression on the face of any of her Jewish friends.

"*We* are in want, not *they!*" she threw out at a group of well-meaning Jewish women who had asked her to come and speak to them on the problems of the Russian Jews.

They were shocked, but many of them were also stirred. They opened their purses to "Henrietta's Russians" and admitted to a grudging admiration of her, though they spoke of Henrietta as being "unladylike."

Henrietta only laughed. Somehow she no longer worried about what the ladies of her father's congregation thought of her. She knew only that she was impelled to do what she was doing; she could do it only her way — with all her strength, her might, her intelligence and her heart.

"But these people have to work all day to live; they can't take time to go to school!" The small Literary Club which Henrietta had joined with others who thought and felt as she did sat discussing the problem of how these people were to learn English.

"Then we'll have to help them to learn at night!" Henrietta insisted.

They were skeptical. "Whoever heard of going to school at night?"

"Are you worried about what people will hear?" Everyone laughed.

"Then we'll open a night school!" the leader suggested.

"Open a night school!" Her mother was a little appalled. "However will you manage to do that?"

"By doing all the hard work herself, naturally!" Bertha said.

"The Literary Club will sponsor it," Henrietta said quickly, but her father smiled. "They're looking for the rooms to rent and trying to get some chairs and tables together to furnish it."

"Who will find the money to pay for it?"

"I've already talked to a few people about donations for that," Henrietta said hastily.

"Who will get the books and work out the program?"

Henrietta looked down at her plate. "I've been working on that."

"And who is going to teach?" Adele's voice piped out louder than all.

Henrietta didn't even have to say a word. They all looked at her and laughed.

"People will help," she said stubbornly.

"Well, I just hope they're worth it," said Maggie who had come in with a shawl for Sadie.

Henrietta sat up straight. This is something she had no doubt about. Her eyes blazed and her voice rang out.

"No one has more right to live than another! Our country is the home of these Russians now, just as it is ours." Though she did not remember getting up, she was standing, and her nostrils flared with her anger.

Maggie stepped back, startled.

"*And none shall make them afraid.*" The words pealed inside Henrietta. She blinked a little at the aptness of them.

Maggie hurried around to pick up the chair Henrietta had toppled over as she rose.

"Queen Victoria!" Maggie said under her breath. "A person would think she's Queen Victoria herself!"

13

"Dear Rachel—"

October 25, 1891

The only thing I can talk about is the opening of the night school. The presumption was that few would come. On Thursday evening, however, we had 205 registered. We can't possibly take in more than 235. Certainly if we had more money, we might rent rooms in the neighborhood.

So far as I personally am concerned, I am my father's daughter. I feel very much drawn to these Russian Jews. . . .

October 31, 1891

I am sure I shall wear you out with the only subject I am able to write about. But console yourself — you would not fare any better if you were here on the spot. I eat, drink and

sleep Russians. Ergo, there is nothing to do
but to write Russians also. In fact the Russian business so absorbs my thoughts that I
have gone back to my early girlish longing
to be a man. I am sure that if I were one I
could mature plans of great benefit to them.

Now my especial fad — the school! As was
predicted, a tremendous rush of pupils came in
on Monday after the holidays! 340 have en-
rolled. As we can with difficulty shelter 300,
a great many were turned away. But the rush
has been so great that we have determined to
rent two rooms elsewhere and open two new
classes. This is of course a serious matter, for
the simple reason that we have no money or
none worth talking about. We shall want two
new teachers, several dozen schoolbooks, slates,
chalk, pencils, besides the rent. . . .

November 8, 1891

The two extra classes of which I wrote decided to open in two large rooms, two squares
away from our building on High Street.

There was a tie in the committee and the
chairman decided in favor of opening. I immediately set to work to think out the problem.

I should like to tell you about those two
days, Monday and Tuesday, in order to give

you an idea of how I spend most of my life.

I rose at 5:30 on Monday morning. At 6:30 I was at my desk, writing to my teachers to meet me earlier than usual, and writing a lengthy letter to two new teachers whom I wish to engage, an answer refusing to lecture and a note to a young lady who had promised to teach but had told me the day before that going out at night was ruinous to her reputation (I told her that her services were no longer needed); besides ringing up Fannie and Tillie Kahn to ask them whether they could substitute that evening. This was before breakfast.

Then to (the Misses Adams') school where I am nowadays busy, recess and all, until three o'clock. Thence I rushed to Cushing's to order the extra books, slates, pencils, etc., for the two new classes, and uptown again for the meeting of the Botany Club which lasts until six. Rushed home for supper, and at seven I was at the Russian school. That evening I had 300 people. But I was thankful to say that by quarter of nine everybody was at work. I reached home at 11:30.

The next morning before breakfast, I had to send out a number of postals for the Botany Club — School — then an hour's meeting with

the Literary Club — then a rush meeting . . .
I had been invited there . . . with the hope
that I might arouse the community in general
to take an interest in the night school. I had
$11 subscribed as annual subscriptions. After
this exciting meeting I barely had time to get
supper before rushing off to the school where
I was to superintend the various classes.
When I reached there, I found that one of the
teachers had sent me a note saying that she
would not be there that evening, as she was
invited to a wedding. I had to teach under the
trying circumstances of being called away once
every ten minutes to attend to some detail of
routine. I again reached home at 11:30 P.M.,
not having had dinner either day.

The only thing I regret is that it is impossible for me to do any reading, not even of the
lightest kind.

Next week I shall write a letter to you in
which the word *Russian* shall not occur . . .

                                   November 15, 1891
The two new classes which we have organ-
ized are fairly at work, and we have since then
had to turn away about 40 pupils for whom we
have no room. . . .

"Henrietta?"

Sadie's voice came faintly from the upstairs bedroom. Henrietta put down her pen. Sadie often
spent whole days in bed, but no one considered her
ailment very serious. She had rheumatism, mostly in
one hand. "All pain but no danger," as Sadie often
said making a face about it.

Sadie's middle room was smaller than either of
the others. Henrietta smiled at the girl stretched out
on the bed. Sadie had often complained of being
the "middle sister" and being put upon by both the
younger and older girls, but she never complained
about having the "middle room." Sadie liked having a room to herself.

"Max," Sadie said, and held up a sheaf of letters
in her hand. "I hope I'll be well before he comes."

"Of course you will." Henrietta plumped up the
pillows and straightened the coverlet. Sadie was still
a little girl, thought Henrietta, even with her talk of
"Max."

He was a young man who had first come to the
Szold house to bring greetings to Papa from Prague
where his family knew friends of the Szolds.

He had come into the narrow hallway, a little daz-
zled by the number of girls about, and talked to Papa.
Sadie, who had not been feeling well, was coming

down the stairway, her dark eyes shining in a pale, wistful face. Max stopped talking and looked up at her, and Sadie stopped right where she was on the stair and held her breath.

He stayed for dinner telling tales of his adventures as a salesman in the United States and Europe.

Afterwards, saying good-by in the hall, he put his hand out to touch the button chain and his fingers unerringly touched the touch button. He was surprised and delighted with the commotion it caused, and the very next time he came he brought a button. A big, broad overcoat button.

Mama was sure the boy had taken it right off his coat. But after that he'd bring a button almost every time he came, and no man could afford to give up that many buttons, Papa said.

He had come again and again whenever he was in Baltimore.

"I'm in love," Sadie whispered.

Henrietta stood up straight. "Max?"

"I think of him all the time. His smile and the way he sort of politely turns his head to listen. He has nice deep eyes. I don't think I've ever seen exactly-hazel eyes like his before. Have you?"

"I've never really noticed his eyes," Henrietta said honestly. She remembered his voice, deep and musical. Its tones carried all the way upstairs when Maggie opened the door to him. "How do you do, Maggie," he always said. Of course, it was Sadie he was coming to see and not Papa. Henrietta hadn't even noticed that.

"You know how love is." Sadie sighed again.

Henrietta looked at her, feeling a little envy.

"I've never been in love."

Sadie sat up. Automatically she rubbed the arm that was stiff and painful without noticing what she was doing. "It's sort of like singing. I mean singing inside. You wake up in the morning and it's there. Like a full orchestra inside you."

Henrietta patted the pillow behind her.

"I guess I've never had that feeling," she said matter-of-factly.

"You know what I think?" Sadie leaned back and stared at the post of her bed. "I think that if one truly loves someone, it isn't important that he love back."

"I'm sure Max loves you back."

"But I mean if he didn't. Even if he didn't, I wouldn't be sorry I was in love." Sadie slid down in the bed. "Of course, I know he does." She grinned suddenly, and it turned into a grimace with a twinge of pain.

Henrietta tucked the covers around her. She moved about the room, straightening the bureau

scarf, gathering the sheets of the sketch book together. She got down on her hands and knees to
pick up the pencil that had rolled under the bed.

"We're engaged."

Henrietta straightened up.

"Only you and Papa know — so far."

Henrietta on her knees leaned over the bed and
kissed Sadie. Suddenly there was a lump in her
throat and she didn't know why. "That's lovely,"
she said standing up.

Sadie giggled. "That's just what Max said you'd
say."

"Well, it's a good thing I didn't disappoint
him."

But if Sadie noticed the tartness in her tone, she
ignored it.

"I hope *I* won't disappoint *him*," Sadie said.

Henrietta laughed softly. "You *couldn't* disappoint anybody!"

Sadie turned a slender face and too-bright eyes to
Henrietta. "I'm hoping not," she said earnestly. "I'm
really hoping not."

A small unexplainable feeling made Henrietta
stand up and move briskly about. "Nonsense." She
picked up more pencils and picked up Sadie's sketch
too. "That's good!"

"Of course it's good." Sadie grinned. Then suddenly she had nothing more to say.

"You'd better go to sleep now." Henrietta bustled about drawing the shades and straightening the bureau top. She put fresh water beside the bed, and left the door slightly ajar as she went out. "So I can hear you, if you need anything."

"I don't need anything," Sadie said. "Except maybe Max." Then she turned her face to the wall.

Slowly Henrietta walked down the hall to her own room. Sadie was grown up too! She gazed at herself in the mirror.

Perhaps the ladies in the front parlor had been right that time after all. Perhaps she was an "old maid." But she didn't feel old-maidish. She grimaced at the caricature that came to mind. There was so much yet she didn't know, so much she needed to do. The road seemed to be stretching out farther and farther ahead of her, instead of shortening.

No matter how much she stared, she couldn't really *see* herself, she thought. And with a wry face, she turned quickly from the mirror and ran downstairs.

14

The Caller

Rachel and Joe came to visit during the spring vacation. When they were ready to leave, Mama cried and Papa wiped his eyes and Henrietta blew her nose several times.

"Henrietta, please come stay with us for awhile. We could have so much fun," Rachel said.

Henrietta shook her head. It was impossible to leave her Russians.

Joe eagerly said, "We would have picnics all the time and we'd do just what you wanted!"

She made a face at him.

"Oh, Henrietta, please come!"

"We would try to walk on both sides of the street at the same time, and turn two corners at once," Joe proposed brightly. "In fact, with you there, in every way we promise to lead a Henriettaish life."

Henrietta laughed. "I'm too busy, really too busy." She waved good-by to them from the doorway and went straight upstairs to her desk in the sitting room. Mama stood at the bottom of the steps, looking after her.

Joe was already a successful young professor at the University of Wisconsin, Henrietta was thinking. His friend, Cyrus Adler, was an instructor in Semitics at Johns Hopkins, and Joe's brother, Morris, was a full professor at the University of Pennsylvania. And she? She was still only a teacher in a girls' school. Restlessly she shoved the papers around on her desk. Not even the Russian Night School, though it had demanded all her extra time and energy, had been sufficient to provide a satisfying goal for her. In a short while it would not even need her anymore. It was running successfully.

Part of her was anxious to hurry on. To what? Henrietta shook herself a little, and settled down to work.

She heard a light tap on the door, and turned. The hours had flown; the shadows had fallen in the room.

Mama's head appeared in the doorway. "Henrietta?" The whisper was loud and somehow conspiratorial. "There's a Mr. Hartogensis here to see you."

Henrietta turned, raising her hands over her head

in a much needed stretch. In spite of herself, she yawned before she said, "He's from the school."

"Oh." Mama sounded disappointed and Henrietta wondered if she had thought that Mr. Hartogensis — Henrietta smiled even before she finished the thought. She had never even thought of Benjamin Hartogensis *that* way. Then she jumped up hurriedly, patted her hair, straightened her skirt and went downstairs.

She scolded him a little for coming out in the rain to see her, and he looked a little crestfallen as she led him into the parlor. Behind him, Mama frowned at her.

She wants me to take him up to the sitting room, thought Henrietta. She looked quickly around the parlor. It was cold and stiff, but she couldn't quite "see" herself sitting cozily with Mr. Hartogensis in the family sitting room.

"Very nice." Mr. Hartogensis looked around nodding and smiling. He examined the wax flowers under the glass dome on the mantel, and looked carefully at the cover of the big album on the high round table in the center of the room. Then he chose a seat opposite the straight-back chair in which she had seated herself. Mama frowned again.

She thinks I should have sat down on the sofa, Henrietta thought, and felt suddenly like a little girl

again, stiff and uncomfortable in the parlor with the
lady callers gazing at her speculatively.

Mama excused herself and Mr. Hartogensis looked
at Henrietta warmly. "She is a very fine woman,
your mother."

Henrietta nodded, eyeing him uneasily. Had he
come to call? or talk about the school? She hoped it
was the school, for somehow she could not think of
him except in connection with it.

Benjamin Hartogensis was an active member of
the Literary Society. He was a businessman. He had
been swept along by her enthusiasm for the work in
the night school and had helped solicit funds for it.
He was red-headed and energetic.

He had interested his friend Louis Levin in the
work also. Louis offered to do the printing for the
school, and soon took over a class in bookkeeping.
A bright young man and an eager teacher, he came
to see Henrietta once about his work and met Bertha.
Now he came to call whenever Bertha was home from
Bryn Mawr.

Henrietta had paid hardly any attention to Benjamin Hartogensis' persistent invitations to walk in
the park or ride in the country. She had suggested
instead that he help another volunteer, Grace Ben-
ham, and was pleased to see them occasionally walking together up the street.

Thinking of Grace, Henrietta found she could look at Benjamin naturally and warmly. "How is Grace?" she asked.

"I am thinking of asking her to marry me." He looked earnestly at her.

Henrietta smiled. She was sincere. "I think that's pretty wonderful."

He sighed. "Yes, I thought that might be what you'd say." He sighed again. Then he sat up straighter. "She is a very lovely person," he said stoutly.

"Oh, she is!"

When he had gone, Henrietta went into the kitchen to tell Mama all about it, and if Mama was disappointed she didn't mention it.

Grace and Benjamin Hartogensis were married, and Henrietta took time to embroider, with exquisitely tiny stitches, a bridal handkerchief for Grace's wedding. She went to the ceremony happily.

But Mama didn't even want to hear about it.

Then suddenly Sadie and Max announced their engagement and the house was again filled with wedding talk and wedding plans.

"Everybody's getting married," said Adele as if they were doing so to spite her.

"You mean *I'm* getting married," said Sadie.

In the back of her mind, Henrietta heard the

Bertha-that-used-to-be in a childish treble — "When I grow up I'm going to get married just like Sadie." And she laughed.

"Oh, I'm not laughing at you," she said quickly to Sadie. "I'm laughing at what I'm thinking about."

"You think too much," her mother said severely. She raised her needle closer to her eyes to thread it.

"That's what all the ladies used to say who came to call." Henrietta held her tongue lightly against the inside of her cheek.

Mama snorted. It sounded just like Rachel.

Henrietta sighed. She had never really gotten over missing Rachel.

"You work too hard," her mother said in the scolding manner she had always used to the little girls.

Henrietta grinned. "Work is beauty, and beauty is truth and truth is life — or something like that."

Bertha gasped. "It's not that way at all." She looked up from her schoolbook. Bertha knew a great deal about almost nothing at all, as Rabbi Szold liked to put it.

" 'Beauty is truth, and truth, beauty' — that's the way the poet, John Keats, said it."

"Well, Henrietta has her own way of saying things," Mama said placidly.

"And she always has a great deal to say too," said Adele, not meaning to be at all complimentary.

Henrietta made a face at her which she happily returned. Adele and she got on very well together, Henrietta reflected.

"As *I* was saying —"

"YOU'RE GOING TO GET MARRIED —" all said together.

Anxiously Sadie looked at her mother. "Do you think Papa would marry us at home?"

"Not in the synagogue?" Mama put her sewing into her lap with surprise. Rachel and Joe had been married in an afternoon ceremony at the synagogue. Both Dr. Jastrow and Rabbi Szold had officiated.

Sadie wriggled her shoulders. "I think it would be nicer at home."

Henrietta looked around at them all gathered in the sitting room. That's what she would like too, she thought, when it happened to her.

"I used to stop and smell the special smell of our house every time I came in," Henrietta said, remembering.

"Our house doesn't smell," said Bertha.

"I said a special smell — a sort of fragrance — something about it," she said vaguely.

"It was probably Mama's pickles leaking in the cellar." Adele's voice was practical.

"It was not."

Bertha giggled.

"Anyway, I for one think it would be lovely to have a wedding in the parlor."

"Oh, not in the parlor," said Sadie. "Papa's study."

Warmly Henrietta smiled at her. "Papa's study."

"Will it be all right with you if we move the big table out of the center of the room so we can all get in?" Mama said politely.

"Oh it will be all right with me, if it's all right with Papa."

"Papa will have to get used to being moved around," Mama said, and sighed a little before she went back to her embroidery.

She meant the new synagogue. There was talk of tearing down the old synagogue and building a new one. But that wasn't what Mama was sighing about, Henrietta knew. There were whispers that it was time to retire Rabbi Szold and get a new Rabbi too, a young one to match the new synagogue.

If there was any worrying to be done, Mama did it. Papa had too much to think about to worry.

His attention, like Henrietta's, was on the Russians. So Mama went ahead with the plans for Sadie's wedding.

15
Sadie

Henrietta sat in the balcony of the synagogue. She leaned forward. Papa was talking about Russia's laws against the Jewish people.

Papa's strong voice carried clearly up from his pulpit.

"You fancy that because we in free America are free, we can repose in peace. I say that so long as a single Jew, in any corner of the earth, can with impunity be insulted on account of his faith, thus long not one Jew anywhere is free . . ."

The words gave Henrietta a strange feeling. They might have been her own. That is the way she felt too. And suddenly she thought of her pompous little speech to Joe so long ago and smiled at the girlishness of it. Joe had been right. "Next year in Jeru-

salem," the closing hope at Passover, were words to
stir the heart and *do* something about.

People who were trying to do something about it
were calling themselves *Zionists.*

The name came from the mountain named Zion
which stood in Palestine. It was the heart of the
Biblical country which had once belonged to the
Jews. Zionists were Jews who wanted to reclaim the
land for their people. They talked excitedly of turning the neglected, worn-out stony treeless country, so
much of it bearing only sand and camels, goats and
donkeys, back into a land of milk and honey. The
two-thousand-year-old hope was the dream of many
of Henrietta's Russians. Was it only a dream?

"I am a Zionist," Henrietta thought in wonder as
she sat in the worn hard seat of her father's synagogue. "I guess I'm a Zionist in my heart of hearts
after all."

"Henrietta?"

Breathlessly Sadie's voice flew up the stairs before
her.

Henrietta put down her pen and turned quickly
from her desk.

Sadie, looking tired and happy, came into the sitting room, her arms piled with boxes. "I can't wait

to show you!" She dumped them all down on the sofa.

"Your trousseau!" Henrietta jumped up. Sadie's slender face was shining. Henrietta looked at her closely. Small beads of perspiration stood on Sadie's forehead.

"Sadie? Are you feeling all right?"

"Fine!" said Sadie, and then she sat down and began to cry. "I'm feeling awful. Just awful. But I was determined to feel good. I was really determined." Suddenly she began to shiver.

In haste, Henrietta half led, half carried her up the crooked narrow stairway to the small middle bedroom on the third floor. She put her to bed.

"I'm going to get Mama, then I'm going to call the doctor."

"Henrietta!" Sadie's voice was the wail of a little girl. "Don't tell Mama. She told me not to get overtired. She told me!"

"Don't be silly," Henrietta said crisply to cover the fright she felt at Sadie's strange manner. "I'll be right back."

Sadie had pneumonia. The doctor left his instructions. Papa came to sit with her and the girls were shooed away. Papa didn't feel well either. For awhile now he had had an illness that came and went. Henrietta looked at her father with a sense of shock. Papa was getting old!

The doctor came again. He came, in all, one hundred times by that day in April. Max came too. One hundred? Two hundred? Three hundred? Henrietta lost count of the times Max came. But it made little difference.

In spite of how often the doctor came, in spite of all that was done — Sadie died.

Mama sat crying like a child. And Papa looked even older.

Henrietta, who was too numb to feel, was too numb to cry and too numb to think. She felt sorriest for Max. For Sadie was gone and he had to go on living without her.

In the end, she cried for Max.

16
Papa

"Hurry, Henrietta!"

Adele waited impatiently at the bottom of the stairs. Papa and Mama and Bertha were already at the new synagogue. Papa had preached his last sermon at the old one long ago. It was Sunday, November 12, 1899. In a few days Papa would be seventy years old.

He spent his mornings carefully writing his scholarly notes, and his afternoons gently snoring in his big black chair. He had a bald spot on the top of his head and wore his vest buttoned up loosely. Papa was sick most of the time, but he wouldn't admit it. He didn't believe in following doctor's orders too closely. He didn't believe he even needed a doctor. Mama bossed and cajoled him, but it didn't do much good.

Henrietta hurried but her thoughts rebelled against the action. It seemed to her that she had been hurrying all the years of her life, and she was still in the same place. A school teacher.

Walking briskly along the street with Adele, she tried to think what it was she had been hurrying toward, but the vision, if there had been one, escaped her. She made a face.

"I wonder if Papa will act surprised," Adele said.

"Why should he act surprised?"

"Because of the honor. Mama said they're going to honor him and there will be all kinds of speeches. Even the mayor will be there. And reporters!"

Henrietta said, "Papa isn't going to act any way but just the way he feels. And I bet he's not going to be surprised."

But he was. Henrietta felt her own surprise as her father stood up there on the new pulpit and received the plaudits of the leaders of the city of Baltimore. He was surprised at the warmth of the people in his congregation and the respectful phrases used to describe his many years of service to the community. He had tears in his eyes when he stepped forward to speak his thanks. Magically, his voice was young and strong and as vibrant as it had ever been when he said the words he had carefully prepared.

Papa had humility, Henrietta thought. She

watched him walking down the aisle, so feeble all at once that he had to be supported on either side by the two men escorting him.

Even though he was known as a leading scholar — his book of commentary on Job was on the shelves of most scholars of the day, and his articles were sought after by many literary journals — the expression of honor surprised and delighted him.

Suddenly Henrietta felt as if she had far to go and much to learn if she were ever to be as much of a person as Papa.

It was strange how much she felt like hurrying again on the way home. Adele could barely keep up with her.

"For heaven's sakes where are you going?"

Henrietta stopped. "I'm not sure. But somewhere!" and started off again with Adele half running beside her.

Miss Charlotte was a little cross when Henrietta resigned. "But you've been here so long," she said.

"I know," Henrietta said. "It's time I left."

"But you are such a good teacher," Miss Ada remonstrated.

"I'm a humbug!" Henrietta explained her feeling to Rachel. "I'm not really a teacher. I don't have the required degree from a university."

"But teachers didn't need a degree when you started!"

"They do now!" Henrietta said. "Times have changed. Just look at the number of girls going to college nowadays. Even Johns Hopkins has a parallel now in Bryn Mawr." Bertha had gone there and Henrietta had helped pay the way, just as she had helped Sadie and was helping Adele.

Henrietta resigned from the directorship of the Russian Night School too. This first night school in the country had been adopted enthusiastically by the city and would be carried on. Now there was no lack of teachers or funds.

"It doesn't need me anymore," Henrietta said to Mama.

But Papa needed her. More than ever. Even though he was no longer writing sermons and was only slowly, laboriously making notes on the margins of the Bible he studied.

Papa was sick a great deal of the time now, and Henrietta went back and forth from Philadelphia to Baltimore working for the Jewish Publication Society. She read manuscripts and proof, edited books for the press, did translations from German, French and Hebrew, wrote reviews and prepared indexes, did revisions, and wrote and wrote and wrote. Her articles were appearing in many different periodicals, and invitations to speak at clubs and societies filled her calendar.

Bertha's marriage to Louis Levin, the young man who had been courting her ever since Henrietta's night school had started, pleased Papa. But Bertha's wedding was the last happy event for him.

Suddenly Papa was terribly sick, and Henrietta flew up and down the stairs, relieving Mama wherever she could. She sat with him most of the night, while Mama tried to sleep, and she often fell asleep, sitting up in the chair. She strengthened herself with the knowledge that she was there if Papa should wake up and need her.

But when he did wake up, for a moment, and called for her, she was not there. Mama had sent her off to bed for a few hours.

Papa died without saying any last word to her, and Henrietta felt bereft — alone as she had never felt alone before.

"Where are you going?" her mother said in surprise when Henrietta rose very early the day after the funeral.

"I'm going to the synagogue to say *Kaddish*." Kaddish was a prayer.

"But Kaddish is always said by the son of the family!" Henrietta knew that too.

Henrietta set her hat squarely on her head. "I was

Papa's only son." She walked off with a stubborn tilt to her jaw.

She went to the synagogue every day, as the custom required, and said the prayer for her father. It was strange, she thought, for the prayer, though it was always said for the dead, was all about life. The word "death" or "dying" was not mentioned in it at all.

Thoughtfully she continued the prayers every Jewish son says for his father.

By living her life, Papa would go on "living" too. She was her father's daughter.

"Now what are you doing?" Adele asked in surprise as Henrietta went immediately from the days of mourning into a flurry of new work.

Henrietta raised her head from a big box of Papa's manuscripts.

"I've decided to be what Papa always wanted me to be — " she explained, feeling happy about it.

"I think you already are everything Papa wanted you to be . . . teacher, writer, organizer, editor, speaker." Adele counted them off on her fingers. "Only yesterday Mama was reading aloud something about you from the newspaper and it said you were one of the 'most learned young women in America!' " She grinned. "Of course they weren't quoting me."

"But I'm not really a scholar. Not like Papa any-way."

Adele viewed the pile of work on the desk. "Well, I guess you will be, when you finish with all that."

Henrietta smiled. "That's what I figure, too. Not that I ever could be as much of one as Papa, of course," she said hastily, catching sight of Adele's face. "But I think I'm going to try." She sat up straight. "I've decided I would get all Papa's writings ready for publication. And to learn enough to do it — I've decided to go to school!"

"Vassar?" Adele was breathless. "I remember you always wanted to go to Vassar."

Henrietta shook her head. "I want to go to the Jewish Theological Seminary in New York."

Adele gasped. "That's a school for Rabbis! Why ever would you want to go to a school for Rabbis?"

The answer seemed obvious enough to Henrietta. "It's the only school that can teach me what I need to know to prepare Papa's work properly."

"I think it's a crazy idea! It's not even *sensible!*"

Henrietta only shrugged. "Maybe it's about time I did something not quite sensible."

"Well, watch your step," Adele advised with fine sarcasm. "Like Mama says, when you do something, you always do it *so* well!"

Henrietta grinned and turned back to her work.

17

The Young Professor

Mama was breathless.

"The wine-colored sofa here; and the big black chair there — " she instructed the moving men.

The chair was Papa's and Mama couldn't bear to leave the house on Lombard Street without it. She took the red rug that had been in the parlor, the round dining-room table and the small Chippendale sofa. Above Henrietta's desk she hung Papa's portrait.

"Where does this go?" The moving man held up a rope of buttons.

The button string. Henrietta looked at it in surprise. Mama had brought the button string to the apartment in New York. Henrietta took it from him and stood there in the midst of boxes and barrels and

wondered what to do with it. She wondered why
Mama had bothered to take it.

"It's part of us." Mama's chin trembled. "All of
you girls — and Sadie — " Her voice broke. "And
Papa too."

Henrietta hung it up. It wasn't what she would
have chosen to remember the house by. She guessed
she would have chosen the fig tree.

She looked around, then out the window to the
busy wide street below. There was no place to plant
a fig tree here. Speculatively she regarded the window ledge where Mama's potted plants from the living room on Lombard Street had been placed. And
smiled at her fancy.

Adele and Henrietta put the things where Mama
wanted. Henrietta didn't care where things were,
just so long as Mama was happy. She noted that the
pink was coming back to Mama's cheeks, and that
she was even beginning to bustle about again. For
a long time after Rabbi Szold had died, she had
wanted to do nothing but sit and sigh.

She had even begun to talk of taking a little trip
with Henrietta — to Europe and maybe even to Palestine. Mama had always wanted to see Palestine.

Their apartment building had a brownstone entrance, and a row of polished brass letter boxes. It
was on West 123rd Street. It was only a few blocks

away from Columbia University's new campus and right across the street from the Jewish Theological Seminary.

Henrietta waited anxiously for her entrance application to be approved. She was working for the Jewish Publication Society, but she was eager to begin Papa's work, too. Getting her father's notes and commentaries in proper order for publication would not be easy. Though she had worked so closely with him for so many years, she felt she did not know enough to do them justice. The class she wished to attend on the study of Talmudic writings would help.

"Pooh!" said Adele. "I don't think they are going to accept your application. I'm sure they won't let a woman into a class meant for Rabbis!"

"Maybe they will," Henrietta said hopefully. "At least I think they might consider it when they take into account my purpose for attending."

But Adele was not hopeful with her at all. Through the days Henrietta waited for the decision, Adele went out and found herself a job. In a publishing office. It was just what she wanted. It was thrilling and it was exciting and she liked New York much better than Baltimore and wished they had made the move years ago.

But Henrietta missed the house on Lombard Street. Her nose no longer found something special to sniff the way it had done when she had entered the house in Baltimore. It hadn't been only the pickles in the cellar, she knew that for sure. It had to do with Papa and Mama together and all of them being there. Henrietta didn't sigh. She didn't miss Papa the way Mama did. He was there always in her mind and her thoughts.

Mama began to make friends; Adele too. Henrietta's companions soon learned the way to Mama's dining-room table, and there they ate and discussed with appetite and fervor.

Mama fussed when Henrietta worked too long and too hard at her editing jobs.

"Why do you always have to drown yourself in every job you do?" Mama scolded.

Henrietta was philosophical. "I guess I just have to," she answered, hardly looking up from the manuscript she was intent on. "I guess that's just me."

"It's your fault, Mama," Adele said brazenly. " 'If you do anything, do it well' — I've heard you say that a thousand times."

"Hmmph." Mama threw her a critical glance. "I don't notice it made any impression on you."

"But it did on Henrietta," Adele said happily. "That's what you're complaining about, isn't it?"

Mama sniffed, and Henrietta had to laugh. "I

don't think it's fair to blame Mama for any idiosyncrasies in my character."

"Well, I'm not blaming her for any in mine either," Adele said quickly.

"I'm taking the credit for only the good things about either of you," Mama said placidly.

Henrietta grinned.

"Are you coming with me to that tea?" Adele looked with disinterest at the work on Henrietta's desk.

"Why not?" said Mama. "Why shouldn't she? I hear some of the professors from the Seminary will be there."

Reluctantly Henrietta put away her work. She didn't really want to meet any of the professors from the Seminary. Not until she knew for certain whether they had decided to let her attend classes there or not. But she went.

She prepared herself for meeting scholars — august professors and doctors of note. She had always been at ease talking with learned men. But she was not prepared for Louis Ginzberg. For one thing, he was not old. He was young, perhaps younger than herself. He had a broad brow and dark curly hair, cut trimly, and a clipped beard like Papa always wore.

Automatically she smiled and held out her hand,

but for some reason she trembled when he shook it
politely, and, for no reason at all, the remembrance
of his gaze as they talked stayed with her all the evening and afterwards all through the night.

"He seems to be quite brilliant," she told her
mother, offhandedly the next day. She crumbled her
bread under her fingers as she talked. "Interesting
looking."

She had been thinking of him all through breakfast. "His eyes are blue. Violet blue."

Then she said hastily as her mother stopped eating
to look at her, "He has a very penetrating mind.
He's working on a book of legends and a number of
other writings besides his teaching."

"That's nice," said Mama and looked carefully
into her plate.

Adele put down her coffee cup. "If you ask me,
he's a conceited ass!"

Mama gasped.

But Henrietta didn't laugh. "I think you're mis-
taken," she said, and finished her breakfast without
saying anything more.

18

An Exceptional Friendship

She saw him again the very next day. Quite by accident. She had been sitting in one of the front rows attending a lecture meeting and had risen quietly to leave early. He was sitting at the end of one of the back rows. Hurrying across the room, down the aisle between the rows of chairs, she stopped suddenly, seeing him.

Hardly knowing that she did it, she held out her hand to him. She saw his surprised face as he half rose to shake her hand, and then overcome with confusion, she hurried out. Her face burned every time she thought of it. But somehow she couldn't avoid looking around for him during the next few days no matter where she went.

She was prompt for her appointment with the head of the Seminary.

"We have decided to allow you to attend any of our classes you need," Dr. Schecter said.

Henrietta smiled.

"But I must tell you that the instructor of the Talmudic class you applied for in particular was strongly opposed to the decision."

Henrietta raised her head.

"Dr. Louis Ginzberg."

"I met him," Henrietta said without any expression.

"But he will abide by our decision, of course."

Henrietta walked slowly home, but she could find only excuses in her heart for him. Naturally he would be opposed to breaking a tradition by opening his class to a woman. She tried to resent his attitude and could not.

She attended his class the first week, sitting far back, but found herself listening with rapt attention. Papa had often talked to her about the Talmud, and she found herself nodding with implicit understanding often when many of the young men in the classroom only looked puzzled.

But she made it a point to hurry out of the classroom as soon as the session was over, and to arrive exactly at the moment it began. She was determined not to ask for any special attention.

But her nights were still sleepless. She put it down

to the excitement of being a student rather than a teacher.

She was a good student. She knew she was as good as any member of the class. She began dreaming of the time when he would say something more than a polite good-morning. With a small smile, perhaps? But something even better than that happened.

He stopped her in the Seminary hall one day and asked whether she would translate an article for him he had written about Dr. Marcus Jastrow.

"He was my father's good friend," she said.

"I know," he said. "But that isn't why I asked you to help me. I ask you because you know German so well and yet you were born here in America. Your English is perfect."

For some reason, she was disappointed at that.

"I'm sorry. I really haven't much spare time."

He smiled, his eyes turning bluer with the sparkle. "It is always the ones who do the most who get the most done. And for you it is probably nothing. It would please me."

She took the article home with her and set everything aside to work on it.

"What are you doing now?" Adele came in very late and yawned as she closed the door.

"It's just a little extra work. A translation." Then she frowned at a line she had written.

"What's the matter?"

"I wonder if I should — " she hesitated, her pen over the paper. "Yes, I will! It is much better this way." She made a small revision.

Adele went on to bed, but Henrietta hardly noticed.

He sent her a note of thanks, and thanked her also for the correction. "I want to tell you what a pleasure it is to have you in my classroom," he added. And signed it. Polite, almost formal — yet she read it several times that night and again the next morning.

Shortly after that he went on a little trip and brought her a Dutch china inkwell. She counted it only a friendly gesture and was pleased to offer to help him outside of class anytime he thought she could.

"You will spoil me," he said. "I've never had anyone working with me who knew what I wanted to say almost before I said it myself!"

She was pleased. "I worked closely with my father. You are a great deal like him."

"I'm going to take that as an honest compliment," he said.

"It is."

Her sincerity made him laugh. "You're not a bit like any of the women I know. Though I must admit

I don't know many. Mostly I know friends of my sister-in-law. I guess I was always too busy learning from books, and now I am not at all unhappy being a bachelor." He smiled warmly at her. "Though I suppose I will marry some day."

She smiled happily back. It was only later she wondered whether he could have meant more than he said.

"What's that?" Adele looked curiously over Henrietta's shoulder.

"Cigars," she said offhandedly.

"Oh," said Adele. She didn't even ask who the cigars were for. Adele knew, thought Henrietta, and recklessly she said, "They are very *good* cigars."

She had brought them from Baltimore after a short visit there. They were the kind Papa had smoked — when he could afford good cigars, that is, or some friend gave him a present. Henrietta thought of Lombard Street and the big stately house on the same square as theirs which belonged to a family named Cone. It had imposing stone steps and an iron gate and inside, she had always imagined, sat the family of Cones around their dinner table exactly as shown on the inside of the cigar box cover.

"The Cones," she said with a smile.

But Adele only shrugged. "When you were gone

someone stopped by to ask whether you'd speak at their club meeting."

This time Henrietta shrugged. "I've decided not to speak much anymore at all." Louis didn't like women to speak in public, but she didn't tell Adele that.

Adele looked at her fixedly. Henrietta knew she had guessed why.

"How old is he anyway?" Adele asked pointedly.

"Oh, not as old as I am," she said airily. But they were no more than good friends, so what did it matter.

"It's not possible for a man and woman to be *just* good friends."

"But he is an exceptional man." Henrietta recalled Dr. Schecter had called him a genius.

Adele said dryly, "And people keep saying you are an exceptional woman."

"So?" Henrietta wondered whether Louis thought she was an exceptional woman.

"So it would have to be a rather exceptional friendship," Adele drawled.

"That's what it is!"

Adele hooted.

And Henrietta kept telling herself that's all it was, though she seemed to be walking around with a symphony inside her.

19

"I'm in Love"

"You *should* be getting out more," Mama scolded. "Not taking on all kinds of extra work."

"I am getting out more. I'm taking walks every day." But Henrietta did not say *who* was walking with her.

"Why don't you invite that nice Dr. Ginzberg to stay for supper some evening," her mother said.

Henrietta did.

After that, Louis came regularly on Tuesdays for supper, and sometimes other nights too. He lived with his brother and sister-in-law farther uptown. On Sunday afternoons he would often come to talk about his work with Henrietta.

They would walk down the long hill to Morningside Park and amble slowly around the solitary paths in the sharp sunshine.

Henrietta never allowed herself to miss walking with him. One Sunday morning, she rose early and found waiting for the afternoon to come almost unbearable. She hastened down the long hill to race around the winding paths in the sensible cold wind by herself. Breathlessly, then, she returned home.

Mama opened the door wide at the sound of her footsteps. "Mr. Hartogensis is here!"

"Benjamin?" Henrietta came in and looked blankly around. He was there — red-headed and just as earnest. But she could hardly see him. His wife Grace had died a few years before, and now, he and his small daughter . . .

She did not really hear him. She made excuses. Even to walk with him. She left him there with Mama while she rushed out to keep her walking date with Louis. "Louis." The name made a singing inside her.

That day they walked together on Riverside. The wind from the river snapped at her veil and tore it off. She tried to pin it back, laughing at the awkwardness of her cold fingers. He tied it for her firmly.

He had brought with him the first pages of a new lecture, and he read them to her as they walked. She listened with every sense. They grew quite warm discussing the ideas in it, and he heard her eagerly.

When their walk was over, he handed the manuscript to her for translation and editing — as if it
were his right. She glowed at the thought of that.
Even though it meant long extra hours at night to
get it done for him. She came home hugging it close
to her.

"He left," said Mama.

"Who?" Henrietta took her veil off carefully without undoing the knot he had made.

"Mr. Hartogensis," Mama said, and pressed her
lips together.

"That's nice," Henrietta said, not even listening
to what Mama said. She carried the veil into her bedroom and put it into her dresser drawer. She opened
the drawer again and again to look at the veil with its
crumpled corner where his knot was tied. She left
the veil there and never wore it again.

She spent her spare moments dreaming. He had
never said anything to her that was more than friendly
interest. But he had *looked*. His gaze was often upon
her in class.

She was pleased when he suggested that she write
a paper on "How the Torah Grows."

She wrote it in one evening, writing it freely and
lucidly, almost as if she were talking to children. The
words she used were simple and meaningful.

Like Papa had often done, Louis only grunted his

satisfaction. But he read parts of it aloud to the
young students in his class:

> 'The Law which Moses commanded us is the
> inheritance of the Congregation of Jacob.'
> This sentence is to be found in the Fifth Book
> of Moses . . . The Hebrew word for Law
> used in the sentence is *Torah*. It became, and
> to this day is, the most important word in the
> dictionary of the Jew . . . An animal does
> what the feeling of the moment wants it to
> do . . . But a real man who feels and thinks
> properly . . . bears in mind his experiences
> of yesterday and many yesterdays, even his
> ancestors' yesterdays, and he takes the mean-
> ing from all the yesterdays he knows, and
> packs it away in a short law, which he can
> easily learn by heart and use on all the to-
> morrows when he and his children need it.
> Such a man says to himself that the foolish
> deeds he does today have to be paid for to-
> morrow. This means there is a proper way
> of living and an improper way of living, and
> the proper way of living is arranged according
> to the laws given by God and used by genera-
> tions upon generations of thinking men . . .

It was *his* vision of Torah and Talmud and he was
pleased to say so. He went on to say what she had
said in her article. Because of the changing condi-

tions of life through the centuries, these basic laws
had been interpreted and elaborated so that the
Torah had grown to its present vast size. The Talmud was the book that held all these explanatory
writings about the Torah.

Like Papa, his thoughts were her thoughts, and
sometimes it was the other way around. Together
they wrote articles, planned revisions and talked
about future work.

People were inviting them together. And they
went arm in arm on the icy streets during their win-
ter walks.

They were close, as close as two people could be
who had never said out loud words of love to each
other.

His first kiss was, oddly, a good-by kiss. His lips
touched her cheek softly and he shook her hand, as
two friends might. He went to Europe for the summer. She sent him long newsy letters; he sent her
warm replies. In one, he said he had shopped a whole
afternoon for a gift for her. Then he wrote to say
he had something very important to tell her.

Henrietta waited for his return.

"I'm in love," she could finally say aloud to herself. And she was awed at the wonder of it.

20
The Bride

Mama and Adele were invited too. Henrietta was glad. She dressed very carefully, pretending it was an ordinary invitation to tea. But she knew it wasn't. It was Louis's sister-in-law who had invited them.

"What's she like?" Adele asked as the three of them walked down the street.

"Oh very nice!" Henrietta said with more enthusiasm than she really felt. The truth was, Louis's sister-in-law had always reminded her of the lady callers on Lombard Street. But she was careful not to say so. It had surprised her that a man so brilliant, so handsome, so idealistic in his research, could be related to such a dull gossipy woman.

"Well, it's certainly nice of her to invite us," Mama said.

Adele made a sound. "Counting the number of suppers Louis has had at our house, I say it's high time!"

"I'm not counting," Mama said.

Henrietta giggled. She couldn't help it.

They pressed the bell of the brownstone entrance which was very much like theirs, and entered the foyer. The Ginzberg apartment was on the second floor. Henrietta had been there only once before, with several members of the class.

There were a good many faculty members there already, Henrietta saw, as they were ushered in by a carefully aproned maid. Henrietta suspected she wore the uniform only for company, for the girl fidgeted with her cap and apron until Henrietta felt fidgety herself.

"Tea?" Henrietta was asked.

She accepted a cup.

"I thought you hated tea!" Adele said.

Henrietta looked down in surprise. "I guess I forgot." A small feeling of dread began to steal over her. She shook herself a little and made a face.

Mama praised the teacakes, and Dr. Schecter reminded them all of Louis's great scholarship, and Henrietta tried not to look at Adele because she knew that Adele was smiling and might question the connection between one and the other. She

smiled instead at Dr. Schecter, and sat there, eager
to ask questions, and yet she could not.

She regarded Louis's sister-in-law. Had she heard
from him?

"Have you heard from him recently?" she heard
herself saying.

A little smile moved her hostess' lips. She looked
coy, as if she knew something no one else did.
"*Quite* recently," she said and then glanced away.

Henrietta wondered whether Louis had written
to his sister about *her*. She felt a little breathless then.

"He's been everywhere!" she said then, boldly.
"The last I heard he was planning to go back to
Frankfurt. He loved Frankfurt," she added. And
wondered why his sister-in-law should throw her an
amused look.

"She thinks I'm being unladylike," Henrietta
thought and smiled to herself at the memories this
brought of Lombard Street.

"He's been busy shopping for gifts," Louis's sister-
in-law said with that playful smile. "He's determined
to bring all his good friends suitable mementos of his
trip."

A strange feeling began to rise within Henrietta.
She sipped a little at the unpleasant taste of the tea.
She wondered why she had not thought to take the
coffee instead. She told herself that the odd feeling

had nothing at all to do with Louis.

"And when is our wanderer returning?" Dr. Schecter set down his cup and looked at Louis's sister-in-law.

"Very soon, very soon," she said mysteriously. Then she stood up very importantly. "In fact, it will be very much sooner than even I suspected."

Henrietta felt surprised. He hadn't written her about any change in plans. She leaned forward eagerly.

"My dear friends, I can't hold it in a moment longer. Louis is engaged."

Adele's hand gripped Henrietta's arm steadyingly as the exclamations rose above her.

Henrietta gave a careful smile.

"I was sure it would be a complete surprise to everyone!" she said and her glance slid over Henrietta.

Something important to tell you. The last letter.

"Well, who is she!" Dr. Schecter's strong voice cut through the twitter. It sounded unusually brusque. So Dr. Schecter must have known too, Henrietta thought painfully, just as Adele did.

"A girl in Frankfurt, and by her picture she is very young and very pretty." Her voice held a triumphant note. It was meant for her, Henrietta knew.

They passed the small photograph around. When

it came her turn, Henrietta glanced at it quickly, afraid to look a moment too long. She saw a girl's face — young, yes, and pretty, the way all young girls are pretty. A younger, prettier edition of herself. The pain was sharp inside her.

"Did it strike you how much she looks like you?" Adele said as they walked home together. Mama had gone on with another friend.

"Does she?" Henrietta's voice was wooden.

Adele looked at her sharply. "Doesn't it make you mad!"

Henrietta allowed herself to shrug. "Why should it?"

"And after all the attention he gave you, too!"

Henrietta heard herself rise to his defense. "We were just good friends. After all, we were working together."

"I bet she doesn't have a brain in her head!"

There was nothing Henrietta could think of to say to that.

"The conceited ass!" Adele sputtered suddenly.

They reached the big square apartment house on 123rd Street, and suddenly Henrietta could hold it in no longer. She ran up the steps and all the way up to the second floor of their apartment where she could be alone.

When Louis returned from Europe, he came immediately to tell Henrietta himself. His eyes filled with light as he talked.

He expected her to be just as happy as he was — because they were friends, thought Henrietta. Friendship? Could it have been only friendship?

She raised her head and looked at him closely. If it had ever been anything more than friendship, he was pretending it had not. And so she pretended too.

"You'll write to her, of course!" he said eagerly. He looked at Henrietta, but he wasn't really seeing her, she thought.

She knew then he had never really "seen" her at all. They had been only friends.

When he had gone, she walked stiffly to her desk, and sat down. She reached for a sheet of note paper. A *letter is talk* — she had often instructed her pupils at the Misses Adams' School. She picked up her pen and began to write.

> Dear Fraulein,
> Dr. Ginzberg was just here and shared with me the joyful . . . he convinced even me that you will make my dear friend happy . . .

She stopped writing and closed her eyes, painfully, a moment, then she forced herself to open them again and finish the letter.

An exceptional friendship had come to an end.

21
Listen to the Fig Tree

Henrietta sat on the deck chair with the rug around her legs and a book held resolutely in front of her face.

"She's been sick." Her mother's cheerful words floated out of the stateroom behind her, and Henrietta made a face. Her mother acted as if Henrietta was recovering from a bout with the measles. Suddenly Henrietta couldn't stand just sitting doing nothing, and with a sudden movement she threw back the rug and bounded across the deck.

"Whoa!" The big voice was backed by a big black coat. She was apologetic.

"That's all right, miss," he said. "But just don't go leaping around like that or next time we'll be having to throw a life ring out toward you."

Henrietta laughed. She walked around the deck

briskly, punishing herself in the cold breeze that was sending everybody into the lounge.

They docked the next morning. Fourteen days on ship. They had been the longest fourteen days of Henrietta's life.

"How do you feel?" her mother said.

Henrietta shrugged. Strange, she had no feelings at all. How was she supposed to feel? "Fine," she said automatically.

"Good," said her mother. "I guess I'm a little excited myself."

Henrietta looked at her mother curiously. She was no longer a young, or even a middle-aged woman. But she was not so old as Henrietta had always thought she was. The notion surprised Henrietta. She seemed to spend the whole day being surprised at little things. As if all at once she possessed a sensitivity she had never known she had.

"Anyway, you've had a good rest," her mother said emphatically, hours later.

Henrietta had never before noticed how her mother continued on with conversations that had never even begun. Mama had always done that, Henrietta realized, but she had just never noticed before.

Suddenly she wondered how many other things she had never noticed.

From Glasgow they went to London, then to

Paris, to Florence and Rome and then Vienna. Everywhere she went she saw Louis in her thoughts. She tried to do more and see more, running away, she knew well, from the thought of him.

"You're different," her old cousins in Vienna said wonderingly.

"I'm older, I guess," Henrietta said gently.

"Thinner and . . ." her Aunt Mina hesitated a moment, "more yourself."

Henrietta opened her eyes wide.

Her aunt nodded her head, wisely, smiling at her. "When you were here with your father, you were an austere young lady. You wouldn't even walk out of the house without putting on your hat. And you knew — my, what a lot you knew!"

For the first time in months, Henrietta laughed loudly. She couldn't remember herself that way at all. And then she could. She made a face. "I guess I've learned that I don't know as much as I thought I knew after all."

"Oh I'm sure you know more," Aunt Mina said. "It just doesn't stick out all over you anymore. Now, you're all of a piece."

Henrietta looked at the embroidery work in Aunt Mina's lap. "You mean cut out of one piece of material?" She mused over the thought.

The older woman shook her head firmly. "Not

at all. That's what's nice about you. You're cut out of many little pieces. Everybody is. But in you, they finally all seem to fit together nicely."

She shook the bit of embroidery out lightly and specks of colored thread flew around. "Finished."

Henrietta wondered if she meant her, or the fancy work. The idea made her smile. But she didn't ask. "Finished?" How strange.

All her life she had been hurrying toward some- thing — what, she had never known. Only lately, she had been spending days and weeks and months — running away. From what?

Herself.

The answer startled her.

"I'm not really all of one piece. All I've been think- ing about this whole trip with Mama is myself."

The old lady leaned forward and touched Henri- etta on the knee. "Your Papa spoke at the synagogue when he was here with you, remember?"

Henrietta thought back. She shook her head.

"I don't remember what it was about exactly either, except one thing. He quoted Hillel, that old teacher who believed so earnestly in Judaism."

Henrietta nodded. Hillel lived at the time of Jesus. She knew then what her aunt was thinking of, for Papa had said it many times.

" 'If I am not for myself — who will be for me?' "

She could almost hear Papa say it.

" 'And if I am only for myself — what am I?

And if not now, when?' "

If not now, when?

The words flooded her mind. They went back, all the way back to the house on Lombard Street, to Papa and the model he unconsciously set up for her. Himself.

"But I am not at all like Papa!"

Her aunt looked at her pertly.

"If you ask me, you're just like your Mama. Half the time I don't know what she's suddenly talking about either!"

Henrietta thought of the dream of her Russians. It was the dream of the Jews she had met in Europe too. Everywhere they went, Jews were earnestly talking of "Next year in Jerusalem."

"It's no dream, if you will it," a young man named Theodor Herzl had said. He had written a book about making the dream come true. He had called the book *The Jewish State.*

"They'll never do it," Uncle Naftalie said.

Automatically, Henrietta said, "You mean *we'll* never do it?"

Her mother gave her an odd look.

"America is not big enough to take in all the refugees in the world," Aunt Mina said, and sighed. "There has to be another 'America' for Jews."

Henrietta looked at her with a warm feeling in her heart. Of course! Why hadn't she thought of it that way before.

She said thoughtfully, "On the Statue of Liberty it says —

> Give me your tired, your poor,
> Your huddled masses yearning to breathe free,
> The wretched refuse of your teeming shore.
> Send these, the homeless, tempest-tossed to me,
> I lift my lamp beside the golden door."

Emma Lazarus had written that.

"A fine American poetess," Aunt Mina said.

"She knew what she was talking about," Mama said. "She was Jewish."

"Theodor Herzl knows what he's talking about, too." Henrietta sat up very straight. Suddenly the land of Israel seemed more than an ancient dream.

A few weeks later, Henrietta and Mama boarded the S.S. *Ismaila* for Beirut. They would sail north to Palestine. They stopped off at Piraeus and joined a Cook's tour to see Athens. Then they sailed across the Mediterranean to Alexandria. A strange impatience began to take hold of Henrietta. She spent many hours walking the decks of the small ship or leaning against the railing peering out over the sea.

Mama said happily, "I guess you've forgotten about him, haven't you?"

Henrietta looked far off to where she would soon catch the first sight of the Palestinian hills. She shook her head.

"No, I haven't forgotten," she answered honestly.

"Well, you don't seem to be thinking about him anymore."

Henrietta looked at her mother. "You don't have to think about something that has become part of you."

Her mother's eyes returned her look in startling clarity. Then she looked away. The soft cheek trembled a little. "That's the way I feel about Papa, too."

Henrietta looked down into the blue waters. Mama took out her handkerchief and blew her nose. Some children chased each other across the deck shrieking. Henrietta smiled at their noisiness.

"Children," Mama said.

Henrietta looked back at them. "I should have had many children of my own."

Mama was peering at the distant horizon. "You will," she said automatically. Her tone was an echo of Lombard Street.

The two women turned to look at each other, and laughed.

The ship sailed north along the coast of Palestine.

"The land of the Philistines," Henrietta murmured as their eyes left the southern desert and looked upon the semitropical coastal strip beyond it.

The ship anchored at Jaffa for a short time, but they did not go ashore there. They had decided to enter Palestine from the north at Beirut and travel by land down through the Holy Land.

"That way we can see it all," Mama said.

Looking out onto Jaffa they could see minarets and palm trees.

"It's the city Jonah set out from before he was swallowed by the whale." Henrietta stared at the rocky coastline of Jaffa.

As the ship moved on, she could make out tumbled Arab houses, white clay cubes streaked with blue, piled on the hillsides. Henrietta stood at the rail, her eyes on the land of vines and fig trees, of hope and history. The land of promise.

"And none shall make them afraid."

Henrietta raised her head, listening.

Mama picked up her embroidery bag. She hadn't heard anything.

"I'll start to get our things together," Henrietta said.

And though Mama said there was plenty of time, Henrietta hurried.

Postscript

The house on Lombard Street is no longer there. Instead there is a grassy parking lot. But some of the houses on that block in Baltimore are still standing and others can be seen like the one in which Henrietta lived.

I saw them. I walked up and down Lombard Street. I visited with some of the members of that family who now live in other parts of Baltimore. In an attic bedroom, I saw Henrietta's old desk. I held the button string and measured its length, and touched the touchbutton. I saw a sketch Sadie had drawn and I read letters in Henrietta's own handwriting. Later, I found a copy of Henrietta's doodling, and read many of her articles and writings.

And then I went to Israel, to the Jewish State that had become a reality, and saw what Henrietta's heart saw when her eyes touched the Land of Promise. Her life found its true work there, and its end, too.

I began to understand what it was that gave the house on Lombard Street its particular magic — the kind of magic which gave Henrietta an enviable strength. She recognized it for what it was almost from the beginning. Though she wasn't able to name it.

Long after she had grown up, she could still separate it from what remained in the trunks and storage boxes — from such things as the pillow cases with Mama's handknit lace, and the cross-stitched towels, the school medals, Papa's snuff box and the button string. She didn't need any of these mementos, for she already had the undefinable *something* she had taken with her from Lombard Street.

But the story doesn't end! you say. No, it doesn't. The stories of true people never end. They go on in the people who come after them, whose lives they have changed by their own.

Henrietta's story will go on. Through the thousands of children she rescued by bringing them to Israel out of the terrorism of Nazi Germany.

Her life work began after she had grown up. It began when she planted her "vine and fig tree" in modern Jerusalem and set to work to do what she knew had to be done. From her efforts came *Hadas-*

sah and the full realization of *Youth Aliyah*.

After her first visit to Israel with her mother, Henrietta Szold went home to organize a helping hand — the volunteer organization of Jewish women called *Hadassah*, "Healer of my people." Through these women in the United States, nurses, doctors, and medical supplies were sent into this land of hope and promise. It is still a helping hand.

More than 300,000 women today belong to Hadassah. The Hadassah Hebrew University Hospital in Jerusalem was built through their work.

Youth Aliyah — *Aliyah* means "going up," or immigrants — was a rescue program that brought young people safely to Israel during the holocaust of Nazi Germany beginning in 1933. To these children, Henrietta Szold was a "Mother in Israel." As long as she lived, she met every boatload of immigrant children arriving in Israel. They were *her* children. She made plans and carried out intricate and sometimes seemingly impossible arrangements for their coming.

But her concern for them did not end with their safe arrival. She set up villages in which they lived, schools in which they learned; she gave them work to do and taught them how to do it. More — she taught them that happiness is not a dream, but something to be found in living each day.

Since its establishment in 1934, Youth Aliyah has brought to Israel more than 120,000 children from many lands. There are 267 Youth Aliyah villages, agricultural settlements and special schools and centers.

Henrietta Szold made her own happiness in doing just what Mama had always done — raising a lot of children.

In honor of this unusual "mother," communities, schools, centers, roads and streets in Israel are named after Henrietta Szold. On her seventy-fifth birthday, she was honored by Mayor La Guardia of New York, and on her eightieth birthday Israel declared a holiday and celebrated with her.

For her eightieth year, hundreds of gifts came from all over the world. Craftsmen sent furniture, artists sent paintings and statues, admirers gave slippers and gloves and shawls, lace collars and cuffs. A bouquet of eighty roses and more than a thousand greetings came, including congratulations from Franklin Roosevelt and Albert Einstein.

And when she was eighty-four years old, this girl from Baltimore was awarded an honorary degree of Doctor of Humanities from the Boston University.

Henrietta Szold lived eighty-five years (1860-1945) and she *lived* up to the last minute. (She was seventy before she took time for the singing lessons she had always promised herself. She took lessons for six months with a concert singer who had settled in Jerusalem, and felt triumphant when she mastered the scale.) To Henrietta, there was always so much more to learn, and so much more to do, and so much further to go.

In all, she went quite a distance. This story leaves out a great many things — you cannot really call it a biography — for it picks and chooses among the events of her life to find her "true" story. Call it only a story. And I hope through reading it, you catch a glimpse of the Henrietta who really was.

Sources

WITH ONLY a few exceptions,* the people named in this story really lived, and the events really happened. Much of course that did happen had to be left out. Many people in Henrietta's life are not even mentioned and many family events are only lightly touched upon, for a great many details which did not directly affect the story had to be omitted. For instance, no mention is made of the two houses the family lived in, for a short time each, just before Rabbi Szold died.

The characterizations of the members of the Szold family are based on a study of letters and conversations with Szold relatives and friends both in the United States and in Israel. For much of the biographical material, the following sources were especially helpful:

Henrietta Szold File, courtesy of The Central Zionist Archives, Jerusalem, Israel.

The Szolds of Lombard Street, by Alexandra Lee Levin (The Jewish Publication Society of America, 1960).

Adele Szold Seltzer's Unpublished Manuscript (two chapters of an unfinished biography), courtesy of The Central Zionist Archives, Jerusalem, Israel.

Henrietta Szold: Life and Letters, by Marvin Lowenthal (New York: Viking Press, 1942).

Woman of Valor, by Irving Fineman (New York: Simon and Schuster, 1961).

Portions of letters appearing in Chapter 10, from *The Szolds of Lombard Street,* by Alexandra Lee Levin (The Jewish Publication Society, 1960).

* A few minor characters and incidents were added for story-telling purposes. Elizabeth Burkley, Frank and Agatha Porter were made-up names. Theresa, Mary and Mr. and Mrs. Albright were made-up names, though such an incident did occur.

Portions of letters appearing in Chapter 13, and miscellaneous excerpts, courtesy of The Central Zionist Archives, Jerusalem, Israel.

Excerpt of letter in Chapter 19, from *Keeper of the Law: Louis Ginzberg,* by Eli Ginzberg (The Jewish Publication Society, 1966).

Reproduction of doodling, courtesy of New York Hadassah.